APPLIED MEDICAL BIBLIOGRAPHY FOR STUDENTS

Publication Number 259
AMERICAN LECTURE SERIES

A Monograph in
The BANNERSTONE DIVISION *of*
AMERICAN LECTURES IN INTERNAL MEDICINE

Edited by
ROSCOE L. PULLEN, A.B., M.D., F.A.C.P.
Professor of Medicine and Dean
University of Missouri School of Medicine
Columbia, Missouri
Consultant to the Surgeon General
Department of the Army
Washington, D.C.

APPLIED MEDICAL BIBLIOGRAPHY

For Students

By

WILLIAM DOSITE POSTELL

Medical Librarian and Professor of Medical Bibliography
Louisiana State University School of Medicine
New Orleans, Louisiana

CHARLES C THOMAS · PUBLISHER
Springfield · Illinois · U.S.A.

CHARLES C THOMAS • PUBLISHER
BANNERSTONE HOUSE
301-327 East Lawrence Avenue, Springfield, Illinois, U.S.A.

Published simultaneously in the British Commonwealth of Nations by
BLACKWELL SCIENTIFIC PUBLICATIONS, LTD., OXFORD, ENGLAND

Published simultaneously in Canada by
THE RYERSON PRESS, TORONTO

Library of Congress Catalog Card Number: 55-8869

Printed in the United States of America

PREFACE

THE LAST two surveys made of medical education emphasized the importance of the library in the development of a sound program of medical education and research. The survey conducted by Herman G. Weiskotten, *et al.,* (1934-1939),* went so far as to state that if a medical school were to be appraised by a single criterion, the library might well serve. This concept of the library's function has placed a greater responsibility on medical educators and librarians to support and develop the library. In order for a student to establish sound methods of study he should have a deep appreciation of the literature of his profession. The time has passed when anyone can walk into a library and, with a cursory glance, survey the literature. The bibliographic approach to medical literature requires the same methodology as any other scientific problem. For a library to be used to advantage, the student must have an understanding of the arrangement and organization of the library, a working knowledge of the principal reference works and indexes, and an appreciation of bibliographic methods. This necessitates some formal instruction in medical bibliography.

The survey of medical schools, conducted by John E. Deitrick and Robert C. Berson (1953),** pointed out that few schools give students instruction in medical bibliography based on the proper educational principles that are the root of instruction in all other departments of the medical school. This is unfortunate, since the failure to recognize medical bibliography as a discipline means that

---

* Weiskotten, H. G., *et al.: Medical Education in the United States, 1934-1939.* Chicago, A. M. A., 1940, 259 pp.

** Survey of Medical Education: *Medical Schools in the United States at Mid-Century.* New York, McGraw-Hill, 1953, 380 pp.

the library is not functioning as an integral part of the educational program. This failure is due in some measure to the lack of interest on the part of the faculty in cooperating with the librarian in this instruction, and also to the librarian who does not organize this course on the basis of applied bibliography. There are still too many didactic lectures supplemented by tours through the library.

A course in medical bibliography can be full of meaning to the student if it is integrated with some phase of his instructional program. Reference tools should be examined with the set purpose of demonstrating to the student how these tools can be utilized. This is the approach to applied bibliography as presented in this text. With the demands made upon the library staff, it is practically impossible for them to give individual attention to all the needs of the faculty and students. In order, therefore, for the students to be able to use the library and its facilities to advantage, formal instruction in applied bibliography is an essential part of their education.

Since the solving of most problems involves the historical approach, the text begins with a brief discussion of the beginnings of medical literature under the heading of Historical Bibliography. The next topic, presented as Modern Bibliography, includes a discussion of reference books, indexes, and periodicals which compose the basic reference collection. No attempt is made to introduce students to foreign language publications. The most common basic reference tools in the English language are the ones the student will first come in contact with, and are the ones he will be introduced to at this time. The final section is entitled Methods of Bibliography and purports to introduce students to the principles of bibliographic citations and the procedures and methods that should be followed in the writing of papers.

To those who have assisted me I wish to acknowledge

their help. I wish to express my appreciation to Miss Nellie Whisenhunt, Instructor in Nursing Education, and Miss Ann Hodge, Service Librarian, School of Medicine, Louisiana State University, for reading the manuscript and offering many helpful suggestions. To Miss Minna Lane, member of the library staff, who has edited my manuscripts for many a year, I am very grateful, and for this latest assistance I am most appreciative. To the students who have patiently listened to my instruction through the years, and who have been the inspiration for this monograph I wish to express my gratitude. It is hoped that this little volume will serve as a guide to the students who must acquire a knowledge of the literature of their profession.

W. D. P.

CONTENTS

PART III

METHODS OF BIBLIOGRAPHY

LIST OF ILLUSTRATIONS

APPLIED MEDICAL BIBLIOGRAPHY FOR STUDENTS

Part I

Historical Bibliography

Plate 1. *Frontispiece.* Thomas Wakley, Father of Modern Medical Journalism.

CHAPTER 1

THE MANUSCRIPT

The Beginnings of Science
Preservation of Greek Culture
Recovery of Greek Culture

THE BEGINNINGS OF SCIENCE

GREEK SCIENCE has its roots in at least two ancient civilizations, those of Mesopotamia and Egypt. These two civilizations were remarkable in the acquisition of positive knowledge in limited spheres. It is to the Sumerians, the original inhabitants of Mesopotamia, that we owe the origin of writing, for underlying the Sumerian civilization was a social order based on the rights of the individual protected by law. This system, due to its highly developed sense of personal property rights, with its need of records and a code of laws for the protection of the individual, brought forth an evolution in writing which was a decisive factor in the development of civilization. The Sumerians obtained their idea of writing from the cylinders which they engraved with various designs to serve as personal seals. Gradually, from these symbols, were developed other symbols to represent words or objects, until at length, writing was perfected as a medium for the recording of speech and thought. Because these writings were recorded on clay tablets, which, when baked, proved almost indestructible, an abundance of written records of the culture of the various Assyro-Babylonian empires was preserved.

The first mention of physicians in Assyrian literature is in the Hammurabi law code, a systematization and codification of all Babylonian laws by Hammurabi, the greatest of the Assyrian kings. In this code, which regulated precisely all phases of life and work in Babylon, it is apparent that physicians not only existed but were held in high esteem. Details of the practice of medicine are derived from the great library of clay tablets, some 30,000 fragments of which are in the British Museum. This collection of records was apparently brought together by King Assurbanipal of Assyria (668-626 B.C.). Their actual age cannot be determined. Several hundred are concerned only with medical matters, but even the most scientific of these tablets reveals the employment of magic rites in the treatment of disease.

In contrast to the Sumerians were the Egyptians, with a dissimilar social and economic background embodying a god-king with absolute control over his subjects. Under this system there was no place for the recognition of private ownership. The earliest records of Egypt were written some centuries later than the first written documents of Mesopotamia, and due to the known commercial and cultural links connecting these two countries, it is logical to assume that the Egyptians imported the art of writing from the Sumerians. The study of Egyptian science is complicated by the fact that the Egyptians wrote with pen and ink on reed-paper, a perishable material. Of all the Egyptian medical literature, which undoubtedly must have been extensive, only five long and well preserved texts are still extant. The two best known manuscripts are the Ebers Papyrus and Edwin Smith Papyrus. The former is chiefly a collection of recipes intended for the use of the physician, and the latter is a collection of surgical case reports for the use of the surgeon.

Another group of Semitic people, the Hebrews, made a distinct contribution to medical science. In the Old Testament of the Bible we learn that Moses had formulated for his people a health code, which amounted to a complete and definite system of public health rules and regulations, and, to enforce it, he selected officials who would correspond to a modern public health staff.

Traditional science was continued by the various European tribes which began to invade continental Greece about 1200 B.C. These tribes, due to their extensive trade relations, soon came in contact with the older civilizations of Mesopotamia and Egypt and the culture of these two countries served as the foundation of Greek science. The geography of the Greek peninsula also played an important role in the development of Greek science. The Greek peninsula is a mountainous country cut up into numerous valleys which were ideal for the growth of the small independent city state. Laws were not made by a semi-divine king but by the citizens in assembly. The gaining of an advantage depended on how well one was versed in the art of argument and logic. The Greeks soon realized that the more facts one had at hand the better one could argue. Therefore, they soon began to make observations, building up a body of factual data. This was the beginning of speculative philosophy, a new and important element in the development of science. The Greeks were the first to attempt to explain nature in terms of everyday experience. Thales (c640-c546 B.C.), an early philosopher, is usually given credit for having been the first to offer an explanation of the nature of matter by proposing that the fundamental material out of which all things are made is water. This was a new thought, and the Greeks enthusiastically began to attempt to explain rationally all nature's laws. The problem was much greater than the Greeks anticipated and in time they emphasized the rational factor at the expense of observation. They never fully developed the technique of experiment, but they were very fertile in the creation of theories.

It remained for the Greek physicians to point the way

to the true scientific method. Hippocrates (b.460 B.C.), the father of medicine, typified the true scientist who first put the rational concept to the test of experiment. This is sometimes called the "Hippocratic Method." Hippocrates was a native of the Island of Cos and from there he wandered to many parts of Greece acquiring a large following and teaching the precepts of his profession. He and his followers actually practiced scientific medicine. They were patient observers of fact and constantly turned to verification from experience, expressed in a record of actual observations. Another famous Greek scientist, Aristotle (384-322 B.C.), gave to science the beginnings of botany, zoology, comparative anatomy and embryology, as well as physiology. He described more than 500 kinds of animals and his biological observations remained unsurpassed for 2000 years.

After the death of Aristotle the center of learning for the ancient world shifted to Alexandria in Egypt. Following the death of Alexander the Great, Ptolemy, one of his generals, became the ruler of Egypt. He and the rulers that followed were patrons of learning. The Museum established by them was a research institution with dissecting rooms, observatories, botanical gardens and libraries. It is generally accepted today that the library contained some 700,000 rolls or volumes, but was eventually destroyed during the wars of conquest which swept over Egypt. When Egypt was absorbed into the Roman Empire in 50 B.C., Alexandria lost its place as the center of learning and Rome succeeded it. Ancient Rome had produced no physician of note through all the years of her existence. The citizen had his domestic herbal and his household god for every disease, and when the Greek physician first came to Italy he was looked upon with contempt and regarded as a mercenary. The Romans soon came to feel, however, that the Greek physicians were indispensable, and in the decree banishing all Greeks from Rome, physicians were specifically exempted. The earliest scientific medical work in Latin is the De Re Medicina of Celsus, a layman, who lived during the second century A.D., and whose work is not original, but is a translation from or a compilation from the Greek. Apparently, it is the sole remaining part of a series of encyclopedic treatises on medicine, agriculture, military hygiene and similar subjects.

The ancient period of medicine closes with the name of the physician who ranks after Hippocrates as the greatest of the Greek physicians. This is Galen (131-201 A.D.), who, notwithstanding all the good he did in the field of experimental physiology, also did a great deal of harm, for he broke down the Hippocratic method of utilizing clinical observations from concrete fact. Galen was a man of great ability and real genius. He had an answer for every problem and he wrote with an assurance which gave succeeding generations the impression that he had said the last word on every phase of medicine. His works are a gigantic encyclopedia of the time.

Unfortunately, the Romans borrowed the results of Greek science without acquiring the method. Consequently, they remained dependent on the intellectual resources of the eastern half of the empire and, when the East was separated from the West, there remained in the West only a scanty store of positive knowledge. Therefore, due to the Roman's ignorance of the method of science and their failure to have ever established a tradition of research, there was precluded the possibility of an education based on nature. The result was the retrogression of science for some centuries to come. This era, known as the Middle Ages, can be considered a period in which a new civilization was born. Classical civilization was sick, but much of it was preserved by the union of the old races with the new vigorous Germanic tribes and a vigorous new religion, Christianity. This new civilization was not created in a short time, but took several centuries of assimilation.

THE PRESERVATION OF GREEK CULTURE

After the disintegration of the Roman Empire the people of Western Europe were without any defense against the hordes of barbarians who swarmed over the country in successive invasions. Crushed by the repeated onslaughts of the Teutonic tribes and left unprotected by the Roman Emperor in the East, the Latin people naturally turned for protection to the church, the last vestige of authority in the western world. The invaders, having scant respect for the works of art and other evidence of Roman culture, destroyed its landmarks. Constant wars and epidemics discouraged any secular interest in science and culture. Both science and culture, therefore, found their only refuge in the monasteries of the church, and these protected and well-built institutions became great storehouses for the countless priceless manuscripts which were entrusted to their care. A few of the monks themselves wrote on medical subjects. St. Isidore of Seville (570-636), the Venerable Bede (674-735) in England, Alcuin (735-804) in France, and Rabanus Maurus (776-856) in Germany, are the names that have come down to us. Pope Sylvester II (d.1003) is the only other writer of merit during this early period in the formation of Western civilization. These works are important as they kept alive, in some measure, the heritage of Greek culture, but one looks in vain for any original contributions to medical science at this time. This was not to come until the culture of classical antiquity was reintroduced into Western Europe by the Arabs during the 10th, 11th, and 12th centuries.

The Byzantine Empire lasted over 1000 years (395-1453), but its only contribution to medicine was to preserve something of the language and culture of the Greeks. The medical literature of this empire is mainly concerned with the compilations of four physicians: Oribasius, Aëtius, Alexander of Tralles, and Paul of Aegina. In 432 the Nestorian Christians were forced to flee from Syria because of religious differences, and they sought refuge in Persia. These refugee scholars established at Gondisapor a school in which translations of Greek works into Syrian and Persian were undertaken. Under the liberal minded rulers a medical school was established which, for centuries, was the most important medical school in the East. The victorious Arabs, who later captured Persia, found at Gondisapor a university where Greek culture and medicine had long been studied and whose professors were chiefly Christians and Jews. With great zeal the Arabs began the translation of the Greek masters into Arabic, further stimulated by Greek scholars who fled to Bagdad, as a result of chaotic world conditions, bringing with them many priceless manuscripts. In this Eastern Caliphate as it was called, three great physicians produced medical writings of note: Rhazes, Haly ben Abbas, and Avicenna. In the Western Caliphate of Arabian conquests, which included Spain, the scientific tradition was established later than in the East. A library and academy was founded at Cordova in 970 and similar institutions sprang up at Toledo and elsewhere until there were at least 70 libraries in Spain. The great physicians of this Caliphate were: Albucasis, Avenzoar, and Moses Maimonides.

RECOVERY OF GREEK CULTURE

During the 11th century and for some centuries to follow, Arabic civilization was looked upon by the scholars of the West as the source of all the learning and science of antiquity. Gradually, a few students sought the centers of Arabic learning and brought back with them glowing accounts of the wisdom of Arabic culture. Thus by the middle of the 11th century, Arabic science was beginning to penetrate into the West. There were at this time two areas of contact between the European and Arabian civilizations: Spain and "The Sicilies." Conditions were similar in the two countries. Most of Spain had been captured by the Arabs and, as Moslem power waned, there remained behind scholars with a knowledge of both Latin and Arabic. The most famous translators were: Abelard of Bath, Gerard of Cremona, and Michael the Scot.

The Sicilian group was less active. The center of translations was at Salerno, which had become a medical center as early as the ninth century. Some element of Greek culture continued in South Italy under the suzerainty of Byzantium. Conquered by the Moslems, Salerno soon became the center of an active lay medical school. During the middle of the 11th century a native of Carthage known as Constantinus Africanus (1020-1087) came to Salerno. He began to translate the Arabic works into Latin and these translations, although crude, were still translations of ideas rather than mere words, and the physicians of Salerno began to study them eagerly. In spite of the opportunities for work and study offered at Salerno, conditions were not exactly to his liking, so he soon journeyed to Monte Cassino, where he became a monk and spent the remainder of his life translating medical works from the Arabic into Latin. Constantin's translations had an invigorating effect on the medical school at Salerno and during the 12th century an extensive medical literature emanated from it, to be known centuries later as the Breslau Codex, containing at least 35 separate works.

From the mass of Arabic-Latin translations, various types of literature resulted. Commentators attempted to compile only the best material from the original authors. Conciliators attempted to reconcile the differences between the contradictions in Hellenist and Arabic doctrine by dialectic means. Others served as concorders, arrangers and harmonizers of outstanding ideas. Concordances written with abbreviated keys to the contents of standard works enjoyed great popularity in the schools. A popular work at this time was the *Summa,* an encyclopedic textbook of medicine, written by many authors and intended for the use of students. An important feature of clinical medicine in the 14th and 15th centuries was the writing of medical case-books known as *Consilia* which consisted of clinical records from the practice of well known physicians and letters of advice written by them to imaginary patients, or to pupils or practitioners who had appealed to them as consultants.

When medical teaching began in the universities, medical manuscripts were added to the libraries. The best known of these libraries was connected with the school at Paris. Others were the Vatican collection of 443 volumes, some of them on medical subjects, the library of the University of Cambridge with 122 volumes, only 5 of which were on medicine, and the library at Peterhouse with 220 volumes, a few of which were on medicine.

Towards the end of the 14th century, Greek manuscripts began to arrive from the East in considerable numbers, carried by refugees from the territories the Turks were occupying and by envoys sent by the Eastern emperors to Italy to solicit aid for Constantinople. These envoys created a desire among the Italians to own more of these manuscripts, and the wealthy accordingly began to send agents to the East for the purpose of purchasing collections. As the period of recovery of these manuscripts drew to a close, another task was necessary. This was the comparison of the numerous Greek manuscripts with each other, with the Latin translations of them from the Arabic, and with the Arabic translations themselves in order that it could be determined how much Greek medicine had been recovered. The scholars of that time found that a great deal was irreparably lost, the most notable example being the works of the Alexandrine school.

Before bringing to a close this brief account, a word should be said in regard to the copying and preservation of the "manuscript." Preparing a manuscript before the invention of printing was a considerable undertaking and very expensive. Scribes were trained in the art of copying and, as the production of manuscripts increased, the universities of Paris and Bologna became great pubishing houses. The writing of a manuscript was a slow and costly procedure for each copy had to be made by hand. A number of persons were engaged on each manuscript. The scribe wrote the text, leaving spaces for initials and sometimes larger spaces for miniatures. The book then went to the rubricator, who put in the paragraph marks and wrote in the chapter headings. The illuminator then painted in the decorative initials and sometimes embellished the first folio with a painted border. Finally, the book might go to a miniaturist, some of whom were very famous, who would paint specimens of his art in the space left for that purpose. The first manuscripts were copied on vellum, but in the late 15th century, after a transitional period in which both materials were used, vellum was replaced by paper. This change and the invention of printing decreased the cost of a book by about 75 per cent and it became possible for all students to own their own texts.

With the invention of printing, the era of the manuscript came to a close and henceforth medical literature adopted the printed page in its various forms for the dissemination of medical knowledge.

CHAPTER 2

THE BOOK

The Medical Book *The Societies*

THE MEDICAL BOOK

THE BEGINNING of the printed book coincided with a number of other important events in world history. In every branch of knowledge tremendous advancements were made. Leonardo da Vinci was artist, anatomist, mathematician, and physicist. Copernicus demonstrated a simpler scheme of cosmogony. Galileo made many discoveries in the field of optics and dynamics. The first printed book was patterned on the old manuscripts and closely resembled the shape of the folio, quarto, and octavo of the Middle Ages. The first type used was the black letter or Gothic, which was cut to resemble the Teutonic handwriting of the period. Later the Roman type, which is in use today, was cut in Italy from the classical handwriting. The books were generally bound in wood covered with leather. The earlier books were printed on parchment or vellum, but paper was later substituted because it was more economical and held ink better.

The earliest medical document produced after the invention of printing was the Gutenberg purgation calendar, printed in 1457 on a half sheet of paper in the type of Gutenberg's 36 line Bible. The year 1467 may properly be regarded as the birthday of the earliest printed medical book for in that year Adolph Rusch printed, at Strassburg, Rabanus Maurus's folio, an encyclopedia which contained a chapter on medicine.

Other medical books which soon followed were translations of Greek and Arabic works brought to Europe by scholars fleeing from the Turks. These translations created a revival in Greek culture which made the works of Galen and, to a lesser extent, the works of Hippocrates seem inspired. The further result was that a group of medical men arose who considered that the final word in medicine had been said by Galen a thousand years before. The period of trying to deduce new meanings and lucid explanations from the passages of Galen lasted for about 70 years from 1470 to 1540. Thus, by 1540, a comparatively representative body of Greek classics had been published in Latin, all of which emphasized the tradition of Galen and showed the same philosophic tendency, with each writer attempting to establish a universal basis for the manifestation of disease.

All of this literature was written and printed for the educated physician. However, surgery had been sharply separated from what is now known as internal medicine and had fallen into the hands of the barbers. Actually, they did most of the work of caring for the sick, but nothing seems to have been printed for them other than reprints of books of recipes, herbals and occasional extracts taken from an original observation. The barber surgeon was trained merely as a guild apprentice. He had no formal education and in particular he knew neither Greek nor Latin, in which all the classics at this time were printed. Between 1535 and 1540, however, there was a most important development in medical writing. Almost simultaneously in three countries important texts were translated or epitomized and printed in the vernacular. Thus the barber surgeon was given access to the classics, and from them he obtained inspiration for the progress which was to be made in the next century.

The first of these books was written by a German physician known as Paracelsus (1493-1541), who is given credit for the innovation of teaching and writing in the vernacular. Far in advance of his time, he discarded Galenism and taught physicians to waste no time on superstition and tradition, but to base their treatments on their own observations. Andreas Vesalius (1514-1564) was probably the most commanding figure in medicine after Galen and before Harvey. Careful study of Galen's works had finally convinced him that the anatomical descriptions in them concerned the monkey, the swine, and the dog, but did not concern man. Therefore, the idea came to him that all that had been written up to this time on human anatomy was wrong, and that a new text was needed based primarily on the anatomy of the human body. He fell upon his task with zeal and enthusiasm, and his great work popularly known as the *Fabrica* was finally published in June, 1543. Ambroise Paré (1510-1590), a great French military surgeon, made the *Fabrica* popular and accessible to the surgeons by writing an epitome of it in the vernacular, and thereby introduced the anatomic discipline into surgery.

The effect of these writings in the vernacular was to turn the minds of men towards realities. Physicians began to observe patients at the bedside and to use their senses for other purposes than studying ancient folios. Formerly it had been considered a sacrilege to dispute any statement which had come out of Greece or Rome, but with the new knowledge available through vernacular writings, physicians began to question many traditional practices and to record observations of their own. The effect of these various publications was to make the medical traditions of the past accessible to the barber surgeons, and also to force from the families, who held medical and surgical secrets, the release of those secrets, making them available not only to the barber surgeons, but also to the more learned and better educated physicians. Thus, the fundamental methods of various types of operations became generally known, and the barber surgeons began to initiate the advances which made surgery through the latter part of the 17th and the entire 18th century a much more dependable guide to therapy than the ideas of the more formally trained physicians. These educated physicians still clung to the philosophic theories and still hoped to discover a fundamental principle, which would explain all internal diseases.

THE SOCIETIES

The progress which medicine made in the 17th century, a period of intense individualism both intellectually and spiritually, was strongly influenced by the spirit of the times. The intellectual atmosphere was clear because of the greater stability of government, the increased domestic peace, and the improved social conditions in all the nations of the world. In the first half of the century the accomplishments of a few scientists and philosophers brought about an unparalleled revolution in established habits of thought and inquiry. In this part of the century the experimental method was created. This method was worked out by amateurs who were interested in experimentation and the improvement of instruments, and by the scientists who began to demonstrate the fallacy of many of the facts handed down from the past. This movement was further encouraged by the philosophers who served as the propagandists.

For a long time many scientists had become dissatisfied because they felt the universities were too conservative in their teachings. The more progressive investigators then conceived the idea of a scientific society which would foster experimental research. This idea of a scientific society first originated in Italy, and part of the idea was that there would be other societies throughout the world which would keep in touch with each other by means of publications. The most important of these early societies was the Accademia dei Lincei at Rome which existed from 1601 to 1630. It was organized by Duke Federigo Cesi in 1601, who was very much interested in the study of bees and plants. After disbanding for a few years they reorganized in 1609 on a more ambitious scale, admitting to membership such men as Peiresc and Galileo. Galileo's affiliations with the society were very close, and he frequently referred to himself as "Academicus." Their transactions were known as *Gesta Lynceorum,* having the distinction of being the earliest (1609) recorded publications of any scientific society.

The second scientific society formed in Italy, the Academy of Experiment (Accademia del Cimento), was organized by the Medicean Grand Duke Ferdinand II and his brother Leopold. The members were for the most part pupils of the disciples of Galileo. These brothers placed their well equipped laboratory and all their instruments at the disposal of the members of the society, and the collaboration of the individual members of the organization was so close that their work is actually that of a group. Their researches were published and became the laboratory manual for the coming generation.

Although the Royal Society of London was not formally organized until 1660, a nucleus of members met as early as 1645. Some of the "philosophers" residing in Oxford formed an organization there in 1648, under the name of the Philosophical Society of Oxford, and met regularly. The Oxford and London Philosophers kept in close touch with each other, but ultimately all activities were concentrated in London, where the meetings were held for the most part at Gresham College. In contrast with the Italian Cimento, the Royal Society was not called into existence by a sovereign power, but developed out of the informal spontaneous meetings of devotees of experimental science, including scholars and amateurs. At this early stage of its history the *Correspondence,* which was actively maintained with continental philosophers, formed an important part of the task of the Society, and selections from it furnished the beginnings of the *Philosophical Transactions* in 1665. The Royal Society, through its work and indeed its very existence, made it clear that a new order had arisen and that former traditional ideas were to be replaced by new facts, new methods of work and new interests. With the publication of its transactions, the Society gave to science that which it needed most, a means of communication, without which scientific progress would have been delayed for decades.

The Académie des Sciences, which came into existence in France in 1666, differed in many respects from the Royal Society of London. The English Society was always in financial difficulties, but the expenses of the French Society were cared for by the royal treasury. Its members were employed on a full time basis to devote themselves to research and were paid fixed salaries. No attempt was made at first by the Academy to issue transactions, but the work of the early years was later collected from the *Journal des Sçavans* and published in 11 volumes. After the Academy was reorganized in 1699 it entered upon a period of great usefulness, reaching its zenith in the middle of the 18th century. During the 17th century as France became the torch bearer of civilization other countries began to copy her laws, customs, and manners. Her Académie became the model of many similar organizations and, therefore, was indirectly responsible for much that was accomplished in succeeding years.

During the 18th century many new scientific and medical societies were founded throughout Europe. In France alone in the latter part of the century, 31 small medical and scientific societies were organized, and in Paris every department of the city had its own society, the most important being the Académie de Chirurgie, founded in 1731. In Germany the Royal Academy at Berlin was founded in 1700, and similar societies were established at Göttingen in 1751 and at Munich in 1759.

In Great Britain a medical society was established at Edinburgh in 1737. The papers read before it by Alexander Monro, primus, combined with his ability as a teacher, led to the rise of Edinburgh as a medical center. John Hunter (1728-1793), the famous British surgeon, established a number of small social clubs, where he could meet his friends and pupils and discuss various medical problems. This practice was followed by other medical men, among them Lettsom, Fothergill, Cooper, and Abernethy. The most famous of these early medical societies was an exclusive Medical Society of seven members organized in 1752 and dominated by William Hunter (1718-1783), the famous English physician. This society published six volumes of its transactions which were entitled, *Medical Observations and Inquiries.* This society was one of the first if not *the* first medical society to publish its transactions.

This briefly is the story of the beginning of the printed medical book and the remaining chapter will be devoted to the development of periodicals or journals as they are referred to in science.

CHAPTER 3

THE JOURNAL

Scientific Journalism

Medical Journalism

American Medical Journalism

SCIENTIFIC JOURNALISM

THE 17TH CENTURY, during which experimental science developed, also witnessed the development of scientific journalism. This was a natural outcome, for the experimental scientist must know the progress others have made in whatever problems are occupying his attention. In the early 17th century the only means of scientific communication was through private correspondence, a method which was almost totally dependent upon the personal relationship between individuals, as well as upon their geographic relation to each other. Such a method was obviously inadequate and scientific periodicals soon began. The scientific journal had its origin in the newspaper, which in turn developed from the news letters which succeeded the *Acta Diurna* or *Daily Doings* of ancient Rome.

The first use of the printing press for journalistic purposes was probably broadsheets, which were quickly gotten out to be sold in the streets as is a special edition of the newspaper today. They were printed on one side and often contained only a single item, such as the account of a battle, a murder, an election, or some other special item of general interest. A member of the medical profession, Dr. Théophrastus Renaudot, a French physician, first conceived the idea of a newspaper in the modern sense of a printed sheet issued at regular intervals. In 1630 he arrived in Paris and obtained permission to open a registry office for the purpose of publishing a gazette.

Scientific journalism, however, did not grow out of the newspaper published by this medical man. Scientists continued to take their discoveries and theories to the scientific societies, in whose transactions they were published. One of the first scientists to conceive of the idea of a regular scientific publication in which scientists could publish their findings and results was Denis de Sallo, a member of the parliament of Paris and a friend of Colbert, Minister to Louis XIV. Sallo submitted his plan for the publication of a weekly scientific periodical to Colbert, who not only approved the plan, but publicly hailed it as a new discovery. The journal appeared January 5, 1665, under the name of the *Journal des Sçavans*. It had five stated purposes, which included the publishing of scientific discoveries and news of interest to the scientific world. How unmistakably the French periodical met a real need can be gathered from the promptness with which the enterprise was copied in England, Italy, Germany, and Holland.

What is believed to be the first medical journal ever published was issued by Nicolas de Blegny entitled *Nouvelles Découverts sur Toutes les Parties de la Médecine,* which appeared in 1679. This journal was published monthly, and speedily became popular among scientific men. It was immediately translated into German and Latin. The first medical journal to appear in English, the *Medicina Curiosa,* was planned like one of the early French journals, the *Journal de Médecine*. It was a small quarto of 56 pages. The first number was published June 16, 1684, and the second and apparently final issue, October 23, of the same year. Medical journalism did not become established at this time, but the end of the 17th century did witness the firm establishment of scientific journalism. These journals were of the greatest assistance in advancing the new ideas for which scientific societies stood. This type of periodical reached a larger group of men than the transactions of scientific societies, and foreshadowed the modern medical and scientific journals. It was not until the 18th century, however, that medical journalism became as firmly established as scientific journalism.

MEDICAL JOURNALISM

Prior to the 18th century those medical journals which appeared had a very brief existence and were mostly little more than the organs of various groups. It was a common practice among editors and publishers to frequently change the titles of their publications in order to maintain interest in them. Thus the *London Medical Journal* became *Medical Facts and Observations* and then the *Medical and Physical Journal*. Nearly all the better journals were translated into other languages and passed through several editions, or rather several printings. The medical journals of this period were not highly scientific, but were written in a popular fashion in order to appeal to the public. Scientific contributions of value were usually published in the transactions of scientific societies or in pamphlet form.

It was not until the latter part of the 18th century, however, that a medical journal, which foreshadowed the development of general medical journals today, was published in England. The first medical journal to become firmly established was the *Medical and Physical Journal of London*, 1799, later edited by Dr. Roderick Macleod, a brilliant scholar. This journal professed to give its readers the most recent information about medicine, surgery, pharmacy, chemistry, and natural history. This journal and the *Medical and Chirurgical Review*, 1794, were in fact the only two journals of any importance until Thomas

Wakley founded *The Lancet* in 1823. *The Lancet* opened a new era. Earlier medical journals had as their stated purpose the diffusion of medical knowledge. This was also the purpose of *The Lancet,* but it also endeavored to make itself the organ of the medical profession by indicating in its columns the direction in which reforms were needed to improve the education and training of physicians, and to maintain proper standards for the profession. The editor was keenly aware of the abuses and injustices then prevailing, and eagerly took upon his shoulders the task of elevating standards of education and the correction of many abuses then apparent. In 1844 the pages of *The Lancet* were enlarged, and in the choice and arrangement of material it became almost the standard pattern of weekly medical journals throughout the British Empire, and even, to a lesser degree, America.

Local medical journals were neither numerous nor successful in towns of England. As early as 1830 attempts were made to start them, but it was not until the latter half of the 19th century that such journals were successfully published for any length of time. Local journals are important in that they stimulate the recording of material which might otherwise be lost, preserve the memories and work of men who have practiced in those places, and also serve as an index to the activities of the medical men in the district.

Medical journalism in other countries developed in about the same manner as in England. The rise of the great French clinicians at the opening of the 18th century caused France and, in particular, Paris, to become the center of medical culture and teaching for almost 50 years. The medical journals founded during this period were on the whole excellent examples of a high type of medical journalism. A new phase in the development of medical literature in Germany occurred at the beginning of the

19th century. Each school of thought, of which there were many new ones, began publication of its own journals, which served as its medium of propaganda. By 1860 Germany was publishing more scientific and medical transactions and periodicals than the rest of the world put together. Journals appeared monthly, weekly, and bimonthly; there were specialty journals and also many local or territorial journals. Some of the local journals were general in character, but most had local characteristics. None of the many journals published were of the caliber of the publications of the Royal Society of London or the Faculty of Medicine of Paris.

AMERICAN MEDICAL JOURNALISM

Prior to the advent of the first medical journal in what is now the United States, only a few medical items had been published. The first medical item published in this country was by a clergyman, Dr. Thomas Thacher. It was issued in the form of a poster and was intended to guide the people of New England in caring for themselves in an epidemic of smallpox which ravaged Boston in 1677-78. A collection of medical writings to appear in Colonial America were the so-called "inoculation pamphlets." These pamphlets were inspired and written either to support the merits or demerits of inoculation as a preventive in smallpox infection. Strangely, it was largely the clergymen who supported the inoculation principle, whereas the physicians were opposed to it. There were only two medical books by American authors published in America before the Revolution. The first was *Every Man His Own Doctor,* probably written by John Tennent; the second, a text on surgery prepared by John Jones for the use of the army in the Revolution. Prior to the establishment of medical periodicals, a physician had little opportunity and less encouragement to record his observations. If he had anything to say to the profession, he had to do it either by a pamphlet printed at his own expense, or had to forward it to someone connected with a medical school or scientific association and trust to him that it would be recorded or otherwise publicized. With the advent of medical journalism these circumstances disappeared, and it is through medical journals that most of the discoveries, which the arts and sciences owe to American physicians, have been made known to the world.

The first medical journals published in the United States were closely connected with the medical schools, as most of the editors held professorships in the colleges. These journals were probably inaugurated to serve as an outlet for their editors' observations and opinions. Practically all of those which lasted for any length of time were published in the North and East, the centers of population and commerce as well as of medical education. The first American medical journal was a quarterly, *The Medical Repository,* which was published in New York from 1797 to 1824. That it met a real need is shown by the fact that in 1800 the demand for earlier volumes had become so great that a second edition or reprint of the first and second volumes was issued, together with a third edition of the same volume in 1804 and 1805. The promoters of this journals were Dr. Elihu H. Smith, a medical writer of note, Dr. Edward Miller, a graduate of the Medical Department of the University of Pennsylvania, and Dr. Samuel L. Mitchill, at that time a professor at Columbia College.

Philadelphia, following the lead of New York, soon began publishing a number of medical journals. In 1804 Dr. John Redman Cox, one of the most scholarly physicians of his time, established the *Philadelphia Medical Museum* which proved very popular. Other journals followed under the editorship of Drs. Tobias Watkins, Nathaniel Potter, Benjamin DeWitt, J. Augustine Smith,

David Hosack, John Wakefield Francis, Valentine Mott, and John Eberle. The finest journal of these early ones proved to be the *Philadelphia Journal of the Medical and Physical Sciences.* It was started by Nathaniel Chapman, a young Virginian who had studied at Edinburgh, and later, under the editorship of Isaac Hays, its name was changed to the *American Journal of the Medical Sciences* under which title it has continued to the present day. At a very early date it merited the respect of the European editors who proclaimed it the equal of any journal published in Europe. Medical journalism west of the Alleghanies is largely associated with the name of Daniel Drake, who was responsible for the issuing or beginning of several journals in the Mississippi Valley.

There were three methods of editing these early journals. Sometimes an editor took over for a publisher and selected material for the journal from contributions which happened to come in. Sometimes associations of physicians were formed and took charge of the editorial work. Finally, the editing of a journal was often the responsibility of a faculty of a school. Although many of the first journals were edited by professors from various schools, a tendency developed later to organize independent journals, which had no connection with schools or societies.

Throughout this early period contributions were voluntary, although some effort was made to obtain material from various localities or sections. A departure from this method was inaugurated when the *American Journal of the Medical Sciences* selected its articles from a large list of authors and even arranged with foreign publishers for regular contributions. As a rule, the journals contained first, original contributions, next, selections or reprints from other journals, American or foreign, then reviews of recent publications and finally news of interest to the profession. The bickering among medical men probably accounts for the short lives of many of the medical journals, the editors falling out among themselves. The relations between the journals, however, were usually friendly, and whatever dissension existed disappeared when any attack from a foreign source concerned American medicine, for intense nationalism was one of their main characteristics. In those days the standard size of the journal was five and one-half by eight and one-half, or six by nine. The volumes consisted of about 500 pages and since they were bound in leather, were more like books than modern periodicals. If a volume proved popular, it was later reprinted, as if it were a book.

With the appearance of the *Journal of the American Medical Association* a change took place in the form of the annual transactions issued by so many medical societies. In 1883 the American Medical Association began publishing its transactions in a weekly journal and soon afterwards medical societies began to follow the move initiated by this Association. A development of periodical literature which occurred during the later part of the 19th century and continued during the 20th was the advent of state journals owned and published by state societies and serving as their official organ. They originated as bulletins of the various state associations, but soon progressed beyond that stage, and most of them now reflect the organizational and scientific endeavors of the organized medical profession of the states.

The most striking development of modern medical periodical literature has been the appearance of a large number of specialty journals. Abstract and review journals have necessarily been compiled due to the tremendous increase in medical periodical literature. Other types of modern medical literature include the transactions of annual meetings of special societies, bulletins of local societies, reports of hospitals and institutions. The annual review volume is becoming popular and is discussed in a later chapter. Medical literature throughout the world is continuing to increase, and the problem now is to organize and index this material in order to make it available to the patrons of science.

Part II

Modern Bibliography

CHAPTER 1

THE MEDICAL LIBRARY AND ITS ORGANIZATION

SINCE MEDICINE today is considered applied biology, a medical collection is not limited to strictly clinical material. The study and practice of medicine is dependent upon advances in related fields of scientific and cultural endeavor, and for that reason a medical library must make available a collection of general, biological, and medical references. A student on being introduced to a medical library for the first time may be somewhat confused by the array of general and special dictionaries and encyclopedias, biographical directories, yearbooks and handbooks, indexes to periodicals, periodicals which range from the scholarly technical journals to the more popular type of magazines, and books including special treatises and monographs, which make up the library's collection. The medical college library can no longer limit its collection to a teaching program, because medical schools in addition to their teaching function have become research centers. The task confronting the medical library is to acquire and make available the enormous amount of literature needed by clinicians, faculty members, research workers, and students. This task is becoming increasingly difficult, for since no library has unlimited funds to purchase the thousands of books and periodicals published each year, a critical selection has to be made. The library then has to arrange its collection in such a manner that the material is accessible to the readers. To carry out this function the collection is first grouped into two divisions, books and periodicals with each arranged according to a definite system.

Books are arranged by subject. There are a number of classification systems. One of the oldest and still the one most commonly used is the Dewey Decimal system. Others that have been devised in later years for medical books are the Boston Medical Library classification, Cunningham's classification for medical literature, and the Armed Forces Medical Library classification, to mention a few. For the purpose of filing, subjects are represented by symbols which may include letters and numbers. In addition to the subject content classification, most libraries follow the practice of assigning special symbols to certain classes of books in order that they may be withdrawn from their regular place on the shelves and grouped separately. The books that a student will first encounter that are so grouped are the reference books. These books usually have the letter "R" as part of their classification number and include dictionaries, encyclopedias, directories, indexes, and other works of this kind. Other collections which are frequently designated by a special symbol and filed separately are those on nursing education and the history of medicine.

Periodicals, due to their enormous increase in number and their importance, are proving to be one of the greatest problems confronting libraries. In order to make them more easily available most libraries file them on the shelves by title or corporate entry. Corporate entry simply refers to the name of the society, institution, or official agency when it occurs as part of the title of a periodical. An example is the *Journal of the Medical Society of New Jersey*. This periodical is filed under Medical Society instead of Journal. Libraries, in order to be consistent in filing periodicals, use some authoritative guide which lists periodicals. The list most commonly used for such a purpose is the *Union List of Serials*. Filing periodicals in such a manner makes locating them simpler than if they were classified, because so many periodicals overlap in their subject content.

Another common practice in arranging material in medical libraries is the grouping of periodicals by current material. Any publication that has appeared within the last five to ten years is usually defined as current. Medicine and its allied sciences are progressing so rapidly that the latest works are the ones referred to most frequently. The latest files are thus made readily available.

In order to facilitate their use, all of the indexes, bibliographic tools, and reference works are arranged in a unit around the information desk. Such tools are the card catalog cabinet, which contains the card index file to the books and, many times, to the periodical listings in the library, and the tube index, if the periodical holdings are listed in this manner. The periodical indexes and often the abstract periodicals will be a part of this unit. The basic reference books also comprise an integral part of this arrangement. Since such tools are the key to the library's collection, such an arrangement is vital to the proper functioning of the library.

The service function of the library usually consists of the loan service, and the reference and bibliographic service. The loan service includes the material that is restricted to use in the library, and that which is circulated or can be checked out. Reference books, certain current periodicals, and rare and valuable works, which cannot be replaced if lost, are usually restricted to use in the library. The loan period varies for the type of material. Current publications usually have a shorter loan period than older works. In some instances different loan periods are assigned books checked out to faculty and students. Reading assignments are in most cases placed on reserve for use in the library or for checking out overnight. The most important duty of the library staff is to assist the readers. At the information desk is a librarian whose duty is to help students use the library to advantage. This is the person the reader should consult in any problem that may arise in the use of the library. The information desired may only require a simple answer, or it may involve a considerable amount of time and research on the part of the librarian. Naturally libraries vary in the kind of reference service they can give. Some libraries are able to offer an extensive bibliographic service including the translation and editing of papers, whereas others must restrict themselves to the ready reference type of information. A library's service is not limited to its own collection. A book not in the collection and needed by one of its patrons may be borrowed from another library through the borrowing privilege known as interlibrary loan.

All libraries have rules and regulations governing the borrowing and use of its material. These rules and regulations have been drawn up from experiences acquired over a period of years in the operation of the library. If some of the rules seem unreasonable it must be borne in mind that there are many types of borrowers using the library, and the rules and regulations have been made with an attempt to be fair to everyone.

CHAPTER 2

INDEXES TO THE BOOK COLLECTION

A BOOK IS A printed and bound volume of some bulk. It is made up of pages consisting of leaves that have been folded a number of times. The size of the book is expressed by the number of times the sheet is folded into leaves or pages. A sheet folded four times is known as a quarto (4to), and makes a book that is approximately square. A book, the sheets of which have been folded eight times is an octavo (8vo) and has an oblong shape, whereas one described as duodecimo (12mo) has had its sheets folded 12 times and is also oblong in shape. On opening a book the first page that is examined is the title page. This page contains so much important information about the book that everyone should develop the habit of examining the title page closely. Following the title of the book is the author's name and frequently his qualifications, which enables the reader to judge his competency as an author. Other data given are the place of publication, publisher, and date of publication. This is referred to as the imprint of the book. There is often confusion between the date of printing and the copyright date. The copyright date appears on the back of the title page and guarantees ownership and protection for the publisher for a period of 28 years with the privilege of renewal for a similar period. The number of copies of a book issued from the same plates is an edition. If more copies are later printed from the same plates they are reprints. A new edition represents changes made in the original book, and a new copyright must be obtained. The book closes with an index. The most common type of index is the dictionary arrangement of names, subjects, and titles. Often the index is divided into an author index and subject index. If the index is to a set of books, reference is made to the volume and page. The volume is frequently given in Roman numerals.

About the middle of the last century book lists of books published for a certain period of time were issued. As book production increased these lists or book guides began to assume a more important role in the book trade making it possible for those interested to keep abreast of what was being published. These tools not only list the books but give the essential bibliographic information such as author, title, place of publication, publisher, date of publication, pages, illustrations, and price. The most commonly used indexes are:

United States Catalog
Cumulative Book Index
Publishers' Trade List Annual
Books in Print
Technical Book Review Index
Monthly Catalog
U.S. Armed Forces Medical Library, *Catalog*

The *United States Catalog* and its supplements are the most comprehensive listing of books published in the English language. The fourth edition is the most frequently used edition of this work and lists books in the English language in print as of January 1, 1928. Its supplements, the *Cumulative Book Index,* issued periodically with cumulative numbers, list books published not only in the United States but also in the English language in other parts of the world. This is a dictionary catalog with entries under author, title, and subject. "See" and "see also" references are included.

Since the *Cumulative Book Index* is often several months in arrears, the latest information on books published and their price can be obtained from book catalogs. The *Publishers' Trade List Annual* is a collection of all the major publishers' catalogs or listings arranged alphabetically by the publisher. It records only books in print and gives price, details, data on discounts, series, illustrations, binding, and other essential information. *Books in Print* is an index to the *Publishers' Trade List Annual* and lists all books in-print for over 600 publishers both by title and author.

The purpose of *Technical Book Review Index* is primarily to identify reviews in current scientific, technical, and trade journals. When it is feasible the reviews are quoted. An author index is included with each annual volume. This publication assists in evaluating books in a special field.

The United States Government is the largest publishing house in this country, and a list of all publications issued by the Government Printing Office is a very important aid to those interested in government publications. This list is entitled the *Monthly Catalog of the United States Government Publications.* The documents are arranged by the issuing agency and each monthly number contains a subject and title index. There is also a cumulative annual index. Recently a decennial cumulative index for the years 1941-1950 was issued. The indexing is alphabetical by subject material and agencies. The usual bibliographic information is given for each title.

An excellent guide to medical books is the Armed Forces Medical Library's *Catalog* published annually which lists books cataloged by the Armed Forces Medical Library. There are two parts to the catalog; the first is an author catalog and the second a subject. In addition to the usual bibliographic information the Armed Forces Medical Library card numbers, subject headings, and classification are given.

One of the most important bibliographic tools in a library is the card catalog which is an index to the library's collection of books, pamphlets, and in some cases periodi-

AUTHOR CARD

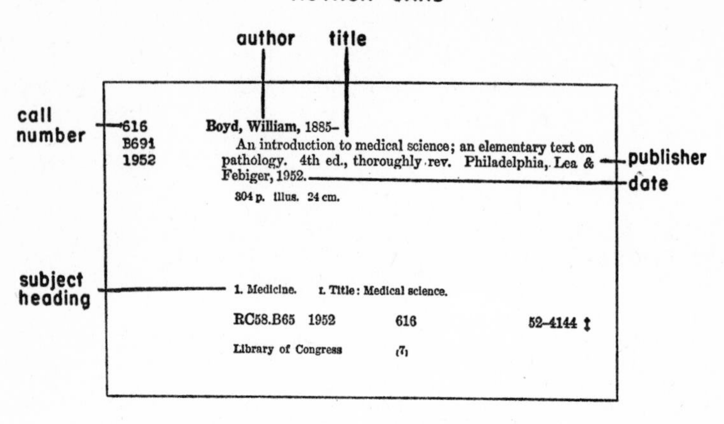

616
B691
1952

Boyd, William, 1885–
An introduction to medical science; an elementary text on pathology. 4th ed., thoroughly rev. Philadelphia, Lea & Febiger, 1952.
304 p. illus. 24 cm.

1. Medicine. I. Title: Medical science.

RC58.B65 1952 616 52-4144 ‡

Library of Congress [7]

TITLE CARD

Medical science.

616
B691
1952

Boyd, William, 1885–
An introduction to medical science; an elementary text on pathology. 4th ed., thoroughly rev. Philadelphia, Lea & Febiger, 1952.
304 p. illus. 24 cm.

1. Medicine. I. Title: Medical science.

RC58.B65 1952 616 52-4144 ‡

Library of Congress [7]

Plate 2

cals. Since new books are constantly being added, it is more convenient to have this index on cards, as it permits the insertion of new titles continually. The catalog follows the dictionary arrangement, the cards for authors, titles, and subjects being arranged alphabetically, except in the case of a divided catalog. In such catalogs the author and subject cards are filed separately.

There are two forms of catalog cards in use in most libraries, the printed Library of Congress cards and the library's own typewritten cards. The Library of Congress cards are printed by the Library of Congress and are avail-

SUBJECT CARD

MEDICINE

616 Boyd, William, 1885–
B691 An introduction to medical science; an elementary text on
1952 pathology. 4th ed., thoroughly rev. Philadelphia, Lea & Febiger, 1952.

304 p. illus. 24 cm.

1. Medicine. I. Title: Medical science.

RC58.B65 1952 616 52-4144 ‡

Library of Congress [7]

Plate 3

able for practically all new books in the English language which are copyrighted. Since cards are frequently not available for old editions the library has to type its own. These cards contain most of the information that will assist the reader in deciding whether this is the book desired or not. On the card is the author, title, and in most cases the imprint of the book. Also given is the pagination, illustrations or diagrams, series or volumes, and, frequently, explanatory notes. The Library of Congress card lists at the bottom the subjects or headings under which additional cards are filed, the copyright number of the book, the order number for the card, the Library of Congress

AUTHOR CARDS

joint authors

```
610.73    Montag, Mildred.
M76n        Nursing arts, by Mildred L. Montag and Margaret Filson.
1953      2d ed.  Philadelphia, Saunders, 1953.
NE          619 p.  illus.  21 cm.

            1. Nurses and nursing.   I. Filson, Margaret, joint author.
          II. Title.
            RT41.M8  1953         610.73              53-5315 ‡
            Library of Congress   [12]
```

```
            Filson, Margaret,    joint author
610.73    Montag, Mildred.
M76n        Nursing arts, by Mildred L. Montag and Margaret Filson.
1953      2d ed.  Philadelphia, Saunders, 1953.
NE          619 p.  illus.  21 cm.

            1. Nurses and nursing.   I. Filson, Margaret, joint author.
          II. Title.
            RT41.M8  1953         610.73              53-5315 ‡
            Library of Congress   [12]
```

Plate 4

classification number, and frequently the Dewey Decimal classification number. In the upper left hand corner of the card is typed the call number of the book. This usually consists of two series of numbers; the upper refers to the subject content, and the lower is the author number.

There are three types of cards: author, title, and subject, thus allowing three separate approaches in locating material. The author cards are so called because the author's name occurs on the first line at the top of the card, and the cards are filed by the author's name. These cards are referred to as the main entry cards, and on the library's typewritten cards this will frequently be the only card with all the bibliographic information. In cases where a book is written by more than one person, each author will have a card filed under his name (Plate 4). Because in so many cases it is easier to remember titles of books rather than authors, libraries follow the practice of filing a card by the title. That is, the title of the book is typed on the top line above the author's name, and the card is filed under the title of the book (Plate 5). Analytical titles are sometimes used since introductory words have no significance as for example Boyd's *An Introduction to Medical Science* (Plate 2). Subject cards, as their title indicates permit the location of a book by subject. In classifying a book, a sufficient number of subject headings are assigned which will adequately cover the subject content. Subject cards are exactly like the author cards only the assigned subject, which is typed in red, is on the top line of the card above the author, and the card is filed by the subject. A book may have only one subject or it may have several (Plates 3 and 5). Since it is not possible to have cards filed under every subject or synonym, cross reference cards are inserted to assist in the location of a desired subject. This type of card is known as the "See" reference card and refers one from a subject which is not used to one that is

TITLE CARD

Nursing arts.

610.73 **Montag, Mildred.**
M76n Nursing arts, by Mildred L. Montag and Margaret Filson.
1953 2d ed. Philadelphia, Saunders, 1953.
NE 619 p. illus. 21 cm.

1. Nurses and nursing. I. Filson, Margaret, joint author.
II. Title.

RT41.M8 1953 610.73 53-5315 ‡

Library of Congress [12]

SUBJECT CARD

NURSES AND NURSING

610.73 **Montag, Mildred.**
M76n Nursing arts, by Mildred L. Montag and Margaret Filson.
1953 2d ed. Philadelphia, Saunders, 1953.
NE 619 p. illus. 21 cm.

1. Nurses and nursing. I. Filson, Margaret, joint author.
II. Title.

RT41.M8 1953 610.73 53-5315 ‡

Library of Congress [12]

Plate 5

used. The second type is the "See also" reference card which refers one to subjects under which additional information may be obtained.

In order for the catalog to be used to advantage a few filing rules are best learned. Alphabetical filing is by the first word except for the articles, a, an, and the. Abbreviations are filed as if they were spelled out, that is, names beginning with M', Mc or St. are filed as if spelled Mac and Saint. The German umlaut is filed as oe for ö and ue for ü. Initials standing for names of associations are filed as if they were spelled out. Hyphenated words are filed as two words, but prefixes with a hyphen are filed as one word. Numerals are arranged as if they were spelled out. Books written by an author are filed alphabetically under his name followed by books about him. The latest edition of a work is always filed first. Libraries differ in many of their filing rules depending on the type of library, but in the main the few rules listed here are generally followed by all libraries.

Chapter 3

BASIC REFERENCE BOOKS

REFERENCE BOOKS should be consulted for some definite piece of information. They are comprehensive in scope and concise in treatment, and are arranged to facilitate the ready and accurate finding of information. There are the more formal reference books such as dictionaries, encyclopedias, statistical works, atlases, directories, and handbooks. The various textbooks and monographs, which stand as "classics" in their respective fields, may also serve as reference tools. Because of the comprehensive presentation of material and the detailed indexing of contents, they will often provide the answer. Such books as Boyd's *Textbook of Pathology* and *Gray's Anatomy* are examples of this type. Any attempt to introduce the reader to this border line class of reference books is beyond the purpose of this work. This chapter will discuss some of the more formal reference works, both general and specialized.

Most reference books used for the finding of specific facts are usually arranged alphabetically, and if not so arranged have a detailed alphabetical index. As the student progresses he will soon realize that the formal reference books are only a part of the reference collection and that some reference questions will involve the use of other books and periodicals in the stacks. In using a reference book the reader should be careful to examine the title page for an evaluation of the author, the publisher, and date of publication. The preface or introduction should be read for information regarding the scope of the work and any special features or limitations. The body of the book should be examined for arrangement of material, entries, cross references, bibliographies, signed articles, and treatment of the subject. A new edition should be checked for the amount of revision, thoroughness, timeliness, and treatment of the subject.

DICTIONARIES

The first reference books that will be discussed are dictionaries which are the main source of information about words, their spelling, pronunciation, meaning, and derivation. The dictionaries considered here are those in the English language, foreign language dictionaries of scientific terms, and dictionaries of special terms, particularly those dealing with science and medicine.

General Dictionaries

Webster, *New International Dictionary of the English Language*

Funk and Wagnalls New Standard Dictionary of the English Language

Webster's *New International Dictionary* and *Funk and Wagnalls New Standard Dictionary* are the two more commonly used unabridged English language dictionaries. Both are arranged alphabetically with separate appendices of additional material. Webster's is the oldest and the most famous of the American dictionaries and generally the most useful. The definitions are given in historical sequence. A special feature is the divided page which contains in the upper part the main words and in the lower various minor words. Funk and Wagnalls emphasizes the current meaning of words, their pronunciation and spelling, and subordinates the historical to the current information.

Special Dictionaries

Webster's Dictionary of Synonyms

Good, *Dictionary of Education*

Fairchild, *Dictionary of Sociology*

Funk and Wagnalls Standard Dictionary of Folklore, Mythology and Legend

Warren, *Dictionary of Psychology*

Harriman, *The New Dictionary of Psychology*

Hinsie and Shatsky, *Psychiatric Dictionary*

Dunning and Davenport, *A Dictionary of Dental Science and Art*

Hackh, *Chemical Dictionary*

Miall and Miall, *A New Dictionary of Chemistry*

Karel and Roach, *A Dictionary of Antibiosis*

Price, *The American Nurses Dictionary*

Special dictionaries serve a very important purpose in the field of science. They supplement the general dictionaries by giving more specific definitions of special and technical terms not included in the general works. There are many dictionaries which may be classed as special and the ones here listed are some of those that are more commonly referred to by the student. *Webster's Dictionary* is a comprehensive dictionary of synonyms including also antonyms. Good's *Dictionary of Education* is a scholarly dictionary defining some 16,000 educational terms and words that have special meaning in the educational field. Fairchild's *Dictionary* gives brief signed articles of definitions of sociological terms. *Funk and Wagnalls Dictionary of Folklore* includes representative selections of folklore cultures of the world. It is useful to psychiatrists and psychologists who are attempting to determine whether certain beliefs in early cultures are similar to the beliefs of psychotic patients. The two psychology dictionaries are those edited by Warren and Harriman. Warren's is the older, authoritative work defining terms used in psychology, while Harriman's is more recent. The *Psychiatric Dictionary* is an excellent and comprehensive work, encyclopedic in its descriptions of psychiatric terms. Dunning and Davenport's *Dental Dictionary* is an excellent book giving pronunciation, derivation, and definition of dental terms. Hackh's *Chemical Dictionary* is one of the most useful and comprehensive of the chemical dictionaries, whereas Miall and Miall's *Dictionary* is a more recent work that will prove useful to the student. Since antibiotics play such an important role in fighting infections Karel and Roach's dictionary of antibiotic terms is a very useful reference. An alphabetically arranged bibliography listing the published reports of antibiotic investigations is included. Price's *Nurses Dictionary* gives definitions and pronunciations of terms used in nursing.

Medical Dictionaries

Blakiston's New Gould Medical Dictionary
Dorland, *The American Illustrated Medical Dictionary*
Stedman's Medical Dictionary

Blakiston's, Dorland's, and Stedman's are the three standard medical dictionaries. They are alphabetically arranged and give definitions, derivations, pronunciations, and illustrations of medical terms.

Bilingual Medical Dictionaries

Marconi and Zino, *Dizionario Inglese-Italiano per le Scienze Mediche*
Lang, *German-English Medical Dictionary*
Schoenewald, *German-English Medical Dictionary*
Gordon, *French-English Medical Dictionary*
Marie, *English, German, French, Italian, Spanish Medical Vocabulary*
Veillon, *Medical Dictionary, Dictionnaire Médical, Medizinisches Wörterbuch*

The bilingual dictionaries of medical terms supplement the general bilingual dictionaries with the technical terminology of medicine. Their main purpose is to serve as an aid in the translation of medical articles in a foreign language or in correspondence involving the use of medical terms. Marconi and Zino's *Dizionario* is a recent Italian dictionary of this type. Lang's *Dictionary* is still considered the best German dictionary although Schoenewald's is the more recent. Gordon's *Dictionary* is an authoritative French-English work although published over 30 years ago. All of these dictionaries have one alphabet, the foreign-English with the exception of Marconi and Zino which is English-Italian; therefore their use is limited. Another type of dictionary which has two or more alphabets serves a multiple purpose. Marie's *Dictionary* presents a selection of medical words with their translations from English into German, French, Italian, and Spanish. The English words are arranged alphabetically with their meaning in the four other languages. Veillon's *Dictionary* probably is the most useful of any as the terms are arranged in three alphabets, English, French, and German. The first part is alphabetically arranged in English with the French and German translations; the second part in French followed by the German and English translations; and the third in German followed by the English and French equivalents.

DIRECTORIES

Directories are among the most important reference tools in any library, and can be classified in two categories. There are the biographical directories, which may be further subdivided into directories of a general nature and of a professional nature; and the directories of hospitals, institutions, schools, and societies. Biographical informatin varies from a mere listing of names and addresses to a rather extensive sketch of the person's life and activities.

Information about institutions and societies is usually brief consisting largely of statistics.

General Directories

Who's Who in America
Who's Who
Current Biography
Who was Who in America
Who was Who
Dictionary of American Biography
Dictionary of National Biography

Who's Who in America, Who's Who, and *Current Biography* are the standard works listing contemporary individuals. *Who's Who in America* is a biographical dictionary of notable living men and women in the United States. *Who's Who* is an annual biographical dictionary limited to Englishmen with the exception of a few prominent personalities of other nationalities. *Current Biography* appears monthly with an annual cumulative volume and is international in scope. *Who was Who in America* and *Who was Who* include prominent individuals who are no longer living. Information given includes names, births, deaths, marriages, positions held, publications, and other pertinent information. *The Dictionary of American Biography* is the outstanding scholarly American biographical dictionary of those noteworthy persons who lived in what is now the United States. It does not include living persons. The *Dictionary of National Biography* is the most important reference work of English biography.

Special Directories

American Dental Directory
Cattell, *American Men of Science*

The *American Dental Directory* is the outstanding national dental directory. It is arranged alphabetically by states, city, and individual. Information provided includes name, address, membership in the American Dental Association, specialty, if any, graduation date, and dental school from which the degree was obtained. The *American Men of Science* lists contemporary outstanding scientists in the basic sciences. Professional but no genealogical or personal data is included. The outstanding scientists are starred.

Medical Directories

American Medical Directory
Directory of Medical Specialists
Kelly and Burrage, *Dictionary of American Medical Biography*
Medical Directory
Who's Who in World Medicine

The *American Medical Directory* is the national directory in medicine. It is divided into three parts. The first includes general information about the American Medical Association, lists of medical schools, examining boards, hospitals approved for training interns, approved residencies and fellowships, medical libraries, medical journals, medical officers in government service, medical societies, and members of special societies. The second part is the directory of physicians and hospitals arranged geographically, and part three is the index of physicians arranged alphabetically. The *Directory of Medical Specialists* is a listing of those who have qualified as specialists by the various American Boards certifying in the medical specialties. Arrangement is alphabetically by board, state, city, and person. Full biographical information is given for each specialist. Additional information includes the certifying qualifications of each board, and the officers of the examining boards. Kelly's *Dictionary* is a biographical dictionary of prominent American physicians and surgeons from Colonial days to 1927. The *Medical Directory* is the

British component of the *American Medical Directory* and lists licensed British practitioners engaged in practice throughout the British Empire. There is no index to physicians which makes it difficult to use since the names are divided according to provinces. Biographical data includes name, address, degrees, positions held, and titles of books and articles published. Other information given includes lists of hospitals, medical societies and medical schools, and the personnel of government health offices. *Who's Who in World Medicine* is an international listing of contemporary prominent physicians. Biographical sketches are short without personal or genealogical information. Its usefulness is limited by the publication date, 1939. Many associations and societies publish directories of their members. They vary as to the amount and kind of information given.

Directories of Institutions and Societies

American Hospital Directory
Catholic Hospital Directory
American Medical Association. Journal: hospital issue, interne and residency issue, and medical education issue.
National Research Council, *Handbook of Scientific and Technical Societies and Institutions*
American Foundations and their Fields
Patterson's American Educational Directory
Schnapper, *American Health Directory*

The *American Hospital Directory* is published as part two of the June issue of *Hospitals.* This is an alphabetical listing by states of civilian hospitals, allied schools, and organizations. General information about the American Hospital Association is given. The *Catholic Hospital Directory* is published as a supplement to *Hospital Progress.* Besides a list of the Catholic hospitals and allied agencies in the United States and Possessions there are sections on

Catholic hospital services, nursing education, education in hospital services, religious organizations engaged in hospital and nursing educational activities, professional and government agencies in hospital service, health care facts and figures, and a purchasing guide and buying directory. The hospital issue of the *Journal of the American Medical Association* is an annual presentation of all statistical and descriptive material relating to hospital services. The interne and residency issue lists the hospitals approved by the American Medical Association for internships and residencies in the various specialties. All the essential information about each hospital is given. The educational issue presents pertinent data relating to medical education in the United States and Canada. The *Handbook of Scientific and Technical Societies and Institutions* lists 1,468 societies giving for each the address, officers, history, purpose, membership, library, research funds, publications, and meetings. The index includes subject classification of the activities, purposes, and research funds of the societies and institutions; a list of current periodicals mentioned; names of research funds, medals, etc., and changes of name in societies and institutions after 1940. *American Foundations and their Fields* gives information about foundations, such as donors, officers and trustees, purpose, activities, assets, expenditures, grants, methods of operations, and other information when known. It is useful for those interested in making application for research grants. *Patterson's Directory* is a comprehensive list of schools by states, educational associations, educational officers of state and local educational systems, and contains a classified directory of schools and a library directory. The *American Health Directory* is a listing of societies and organizations that deal with health problems. Information given for each society includes, name, address, and publications. The societies are grouped under subject divisions.

This work is very useful in locating addresses of little known organizations.

ENCYCLOPEDIAS

Encyclopedias are works in which the various branches of knowledge are treated separately and are usually arranged alphabetically. For the purpose of this study encyclopedias have been grouped into general, special, medical, and pharmaceutical. The encyclopedia which deals with special subjects is becoming more popular today as knowledge tends to become more specialized. The medical encyclopedias are not as numerous as they were several years ago. No doubt our highly specialized knowledge is making it difficult to treat medical topics as a part of a general work. This listing presents those encyclopedias which are more commonly used by students.

General Encyclopedias

Encyclopedia Americana

Encyclopaedia Britannica

The *Americana* is an excellent work. Its alphabetical arrangement is by words. There is a classified index volume which is needed to locate small subjects not covered by cross references. It is especially good in the field of science and technology. The *Britannica* is the most scholarly encyclopedia in English. Its alphabetical arrangement is by letter, and since the information is grouped under large subjects, the index volume is essential for locating small subjects.

Special Encyclopedias

Encyclopedia of Nursing

Encyclopedia of the Social Sciences

Gaynor, *Pocket Encyclopedia of Atomic Energy*

Langer, *An Encyclopedia of World History*

Monroe, *Encyclopedia of Educational Research*

The *Encyclopedia of Nursing* is a one volume work on nursing. Emphasis is on nursing and the application of general and scientific terms to nursing methods and to nursing education. Descriptions of terms are brief. The *Encyclopedia of the Social Sciences* is a comprehensive encyclopedia of the whole field of the social sciences. Its purpose is to cover all important topics in the fields of political science, economics, law, anthropology, sociology, penology, and social work, and the social aspects of ethics, education, philosophy, psychology, biology, geography, medicine, and art. It is international in scope but emphasizes the English speaking countries and western Europe rather than other regions or interests. The purpose of Gaynor's *Encyclopedia of Atomic Energy* is to present a comprehensive collection of brief definitions and explanations of the terms and expressions in this field to the layman with a good average education, and to the student with a fair working knowledge of physics and an acquaintance with higher mathematics. Langer's *Encyclopedia* is a new version of Ploetz's *Manual of Universal History* and has been largely rewritten so that now it is an epitome of world history. Monroe's *Encyclopedia* is a critical synthesis of the literature of educational research arranged alphabetically by subject. It is particularly useful for its selective bibliographies.

Medical Encyclopedias

Cyclopedia of Medicine, Surgery, Specialties
Brennemann, *Practice of Pediatrics*
Davis, *Gynecology and Obstetrics*
Lewis, *Practice of Surgery*
Tice, *Practice of Medicine*
The Oxford Medicine

All the above encyclopedias are of the loose-leaf variety which is still quite popular in medicine, although not as popular as it has been. The principal advantage of this form is that parts or sections may be revised as necessary and inserted in the work without revising the entire set. The reader should be careful to note any recorded dates in order to evaluate the timeliness of the material. Unfortunately, these revisions are frequently not dated which makes it difficult for the reader to determine the date of issue. The *Cyclopedia of Medicine* is a dictionary arranged 14 volume set of good comprehensive articles emphasizing clinical medicine with a separate *Desk Index Volume.* An *Annual Service Volume* is issued which discusses the noteworthy advances that have occurred during that year. Brennemann, Davis, Lewis, and Tice are all publications of the W. F. Prior Company. They are good comprehensive systems, well illustrated, with alphabetically arranged general and supplementary subject indexes. References are to volume, chapter, and page. *Oxford Medicine* is a good loose-leaf system of medicine by English and American specialists. It is well illustrated and the bibliographies are good. In this set the pages are dated so it is easy to determine when a revision was made. There is a dictionary arranged author and subject index in a separate volume. A supplementary index has been issued covering the more recent revisions.

Pharmacopoeias, Dispensatories, and Unofficial List of Drugs

The Pharmacopoeia of the United States of America
The Dispensatory of the United States of America
The National Formulary
Merck Index
Modern Drug Encyclopedia and Therapeutic Index

There are three types of publications dealing with drugs. The first is the official recognized authoritative work on standards for drugs and other material used in the treatment and prevention of disease. The second supplements the official list and discusses in detail the substances listed in the official works. The third is the drug encyclopedia which describes the many unofficial drug preparations on the market. The *Pharmacopoeia of the United States* is the standard list of official therapeutic agents in this country. A new edition now appears every three to five years. The contents include sections devoted to the work of the national convention, additions and deletions since the last edition, general tests, processes and apparatus, reagents and test solutions, and useful tables of atomic and molecular weights. Supplements are issued between revisions listing new drugs and preparations. *The National Formulary* supplements the *Pharmacopoeia* by listing drugs not important enough to be included in the *Pharmacopoeia* but of sufficient value to be standardized. Its contents closely resemble the latter work. The *Dispensatory of the United States of America* discusses in much greater detail the drugs and preparations listed in the *United States Pharmacopoeia,* the *Pharmacopoeia of Great Britain* and the *National Formulary*. In addition, a large number of unofficial drugs, veterinary doses, general tests, and tables are included and discussed. The *Merck Index* contains useful scientific data on the physical, chemical, and medicinal properties of approximately 8,000 chemicals, clinicochemical reactions, tests and reagents, formulas of preparations of culture media, fixatives and staining solutions, tables, antidotes for poisons, and literature references. The *Modern Drug Encyclopedia and Therapeutic Index* presents descriptions of modern, non-pharmacopeal medicinal preparations in thousands of forms. The latest (5th) edition describes 1,475 newly introduced drugs, biologicals, and allergens introduced since the appearance of the 4th edition. It is kept up to date by *Modern Drugs,* a quarterly supplement service.

YEARBOOKS

Yearbooks are published in many fields. Some serve as supplements to standard encyclopedias whereas others appear every year as annual volumes covering some phase of knowledge. For the purpose of this study yearbooks are treated under the headings of general, special, and medical. Yearbooks are becoming more popular in reviewing progress in the arts and sciences for the year, and the number issued is increasing yearly.

General Yearbooks

Americana Annual *Britannica Book of the Year*

The *Americana* and the *Britannica* are supplements to their respective encyclopedias. They both record events of the year previous to the date on the title page, and serve as an annual record of progress and events in a given subject.

Special Yearbooks

Social Work Year Book *Statistical Abstract of the United States*
World Almanac and Book of Facts

This group includes a number of miscellaneous annuals frequently referred to by the student. *The Social Work Year Book* describes organized activities in social work and the various related fields. The work is divided into two parts: part one contains topical articles descriptive of functions, organized activities, and programs, whereas part two is a directory of national social agencies. The *Statistical Abstract* presents the quantitative summary of statistics on the political, social, industrial, and economic organization of the United States. The *World Almanac* is the most comprehensive and most frequently used of the almanacs for miscellaneous information. It is a very useful work which covers statistical data on social, political, financial, religious, educational, and other subjects. There is an alphabetically arranged index at the beginning of each volume.

Medical Yearbooks

Current Therapy
Monographs on Surgery
New and Nonofficial Remedies
Physicians' Desk Reference

Yearbooks in medicine cover a wide range of subjects. There is hardly a phase of medicine and the allied sciences that does not have its own yearbook. They are known under various titles as Yearbooks, Annual Reviews, Advances in, and Progress in, to mention a few. This type of material presents a problem for librarians, since they can be considered either as books or periodicals. Their format is that of a book, but since they are issued periodically they are serials. Because of their failure to be indexed regularly in the periodical indexes and because these indexes are frequently late in appearing, many libraries classify them as books. For the purpose of this study, however, they will be discussed in the chapter on periodicals. Only a few that are not generally considered periodicals will be discussed here. *Current Therapy* summarizes the advances made in new drugs with an interpretation and evaluation of these advances. Diagnosis, unless it is an integral part of therapy is not discussed. The authors present their methods of treating each disease whether it is new or a long established one. All discussions of treatment are by recognized authorities. *Monographs on Surgery* has replaced the previously published *Nelson's Loose-Leaf Surgery*. The articles discuss recent advances in general surgery, gynecology, urology, and orthopedics. *New and Nonofficial Remedies* supplements the *Pharmacopoeia of the United States,* the

National Formulary, and the *Dispensatory of the United States of America,* giving information on non-official proprietary and non-proprietary drugs and preparations. This is a very valuable list of drugs which is particularly useful during the interval between the appearance of the *Pharmacopoeia* and the *National Formulary*. The *Physicians' Desk Reference* is divided into five sections. Section one is an alphabetical index of brands and manufacturers; section two, an index of drugs, chemical and pharmacological products; section three, a therapeutic indications index; section four, professional products information; and section five, general professional information. This reference work is useful in enabling the student to keep abreast of changes in the formulae and the appearance of new drugs and new specialty products.

CHAPTER 4

INDEXES TO THE PERIODICAL COLLECTION

PERIODICALS serve a very important function in supplying reference material for the student, since reference work in medicine is so largely concerned with current information. A library should have three types of reference aids in order to answer the ordinary questions about periodicals. First, a bibliography or catalog which lists the periodicals themselves and is not an index to their contents. These catalogs give the title, character, history, editors, price, publisher, and frequently other information that will prove useful to the reader. The second reference aid is a list of the holdings or serial record of the library. These listings may be entered on cards and filed in the catalog cabinet, a special file, or entered on what is referred to as a tube index. The indexes to the contents of the periodicals themselves are the third reference aid.

BIBLIOGRAPHY OF PERIODICALS

Ulrich's Periodicals Directory
Union List of Serials
World Medical Periodicals
World List of Scientific Periodicals

Ulrich's Directory is a classified guide to a selected list of current periodicals both foreign and domestic. The periodicals are arranged alphabetically under subject classification. Each entry includes title, sub-title, date or origin, frequency, price, publisher and place of publication, annual index, cumulative indexes, and items characteristic of each periodical. A list of the indexes which index the periodical is included as part of the information given about each journal. There is a title index to the periodicals included in this directory. The *Union List of Serials* is the most important and comprehensive list of holdings in the libraries of the United States and Canada. It lists between 115,000 and 120,000 titles in about 600 libraries. Information given includes the title of the journal, place of publication, and in some cases the publisher, the date publication began, whether it is a continuation or has ceased publication, publication history, and holdings of the cooperating libraries. Arrangement is alphabetical by corporate entry. The *World Medical Periodicals* is an international list of all current medical periodicals, all medico-biological periodicals regularly surveyed by certain abstracting agencies, and well-known medical journals which ceased publication during the period 1900-1950. Each entry includes title, place of publication, language or languages of publication, frequency, symbols indicating which of the principal abstracting services regularly survey the periodicals, and the *World List* abbreviation of the title. The *World List of Scientific Periodicals* is an alphabetical listing by title in the natural sciences showing location of about 50,000 titles in 247 libraries in Great Britain. The list includes all such periodicals issued between 1900-1950. Also entered are titles which so far as is known are not available in Great Britain. This work is therefore a bibliography as well as a union list.

SERIAL RECORD

Card File | Tube Index File

The Serial Record lists all of the serial titles in the library. The information given for each title usually includes the volumes and numbers with their dates that are present in the library's holdings. Additional information that may be given is the first year of publication and the

ENTRY SHOWING COMPLETE FILE IS AVAILABLE

T.M.L.

Journal of clinical endocrinology

v.1-11 1941-51

Continued as Journal of clinical endocrinology & metabolism

ENTRY SHOWING PARTIAL HOLDINGS AVAILABLE

T.M.L.

Journal of colloid science

v.5 1950 #5

Plate 6

last year if the journal is a closed file. The serial record may also indicate any changes in the name of a periodical as for example *Southern Surgeon* was continued with volume 17 as *American Surgeon.* The card for *American Surgeon* indicates that volume 1-16 was published as *Southern Surgeon.* Frequently there are two listings, an alphabetical arrangement by title or corporate entry and a subject list where each title is listed under a specific subject. If there

ENTRY SHOWING COMPLETE FILE IS AVAILABLE

J.Allergy v.1- *date* 1929/0- *date*

ENTRY SHOWING PARTIAL HOLDINGS AVAILABLE

Milbank Mem.Fund,Quart.Bull.

v.1 1923 *no.3-4*	v.4 1926 *no.1-3*	v.19 1941
v.2 1924 *no.1-3*	v.5-17 1926-29	v.20 1942 *no.1-2,4*
v.3 1925 *no.1,3-4*	v.18 1940 *no.1-3*	v.21-*date*-1943-*date*

Plate 7

is any possibility of confusion in the list of a title, see cards are added to facilitate its location.

Libraries follow different practices in listing their holdings. Some make use of catalog cards, others tube indexes, to mention the two most popular methods. The card is the standard 3 by 5 and may be filed either as part of the entire book collection or in a separate file. In either case it is filed in the card catalog cabinet. Examples of serial record cards as given in Plate 6 are those of the Rudolph Matas Medical Library of Tulane University. The top card gives the complete holdings with the continuation title. The bottom card represents an incomplete file. The notation in script gives the exact number that is available.

The tube index, the other method commonly used of recording the library's holdings, takes its name from the celluloid tubes into which are inserted the listings of the periodicals which in turn are inserted in leaves and mounted on a stand. Examples of tube index entries of the Louisiana State University School of Medicine Library are given in Plate 7. Complete volumes are noted in typed numbers whereas incomplete volumes are recorded in pencil in order that they may be easily changed when new numbers are added. The symbol -date signifies that the library's holdings are complete from that volume and date to the currently received number.

INDEXES TO PERIODICAL CONTENTS

It became quite obvious that as periodicals continued to increase in number indexes to their contents must be compiled if the material was to be available to students and scholars. Therefore very early in the history of periodical literature such indexes appeared. Later as the literature broadened, numerous special indexes in many of the arts and sciences were compiled. There are a number of points which determine the value of an index to periodicals among which are: the scope of the index, the length of period covered, the frequency and promptness of publication, and the completeness and quality of the indexing. The scope of the index refers to whether the indexes are general or devoted to a particular subject or specialized field. In this study more attention will be given to the specialized indexes that cover the field of medicine and allied sciences. The length of period covered is significant since it is more important to use an index which indexes periodicals for a long period of time rather than one that indexes material for a short period. Frequency and promptness must be considered since this refers to the timeliness of the material indexed. Completeness takes into consideration whether all articles in a periodical are indexed or whether a selection is made. Quality refers to the method and convenience of arrangement. The indexes to be considered here are general, special, medical, historical, cumulative indexes of journals, and abstract journals.

General Indexes

Readers' Guide to Periodical Literature

International Index to Periodicals

The *Readers' Guide* indexes about 125 general and popular periodicals as well as some scientific and scholarly publications. It is useful for popular literature on medical and near medical subjects, also for articles concerning physicians. Its special features are full dictionary cataloging of all articles, listed under author, subject, and title when necessary. It appears semi-monthly from September to June, and monthly in July and August. It is cumulative at intervals until the last number of each current volume which covers the year and forms a new annual volume. Permanently cumulated volumes are issued at longer intervals. The *International Index* is organized along the same plan as the *Readers' Guide*. It indexes the more scholarly periodicals in the humanities and science. The cumulative number appears four times a year with an annual and a permanent cumulative volume every three years. Reference to all periodicals in these two indexes is to volume, page, and date.

Special Indexes

Public Affairs Information Service. Bulletin

Education Index

Index of Hospital Literature

Index to Dental Literature

There are numerous special indexes to the periodical literature. The ones listed here are some that the student will have occasion to use. The *Public Affairs Information Service. Bulletin* is a cooperative clearing house of public affairs information. It is a very useful subject index of political science, government, legislation, economics, and sociology for the lay and the professional reader. Pamphlets and multigraphed material are indexed as well as periodical literature. Cumulations appear five times a year with the last number becoming the annual cumulation. *Education Index* is a cumulative author and subject index to a selected list of about 150 education periodicals. It is published monthly except June and August with annual and triennial cumulations. In addition to the references to periodicals, many references to books, pamphlets, and society transactions are included. The *Index of Hospital Literature* is an alphabetically arranged author and subject index of about 130 journals whose articles relate to hospitals and their work. The numbers appear semi-annually and for 1945-1949 a five year cumulative volume was issued. The *Index to Dental Literature* covers the period from 1839 to date. One hundred and forty-four dental journals are indexed and since 1939 the arrangement has been alphabetical by author and subject. It was issued in three to five year intervals from 1921 to 1947, and biennially from 1948 to 1949. Since 1950 it has appeared quarterly with an annual cumulation. No foreign periodicals are indexed.

Medical Indexes

Index-Catalogue of the Library of the Surgeon General's Office
Index Medicus
Quarterly Cumulative Index to Current Medical Literature
Quarterly Cumulative Index Medicus
Current List of Medical Literature

BROCKBANK, WILLIAM. Bicentenary of the Manchester Royal Infirmary. Brit. M.J. 2: 88-90, July 12, 1952. Also in Nurs.Times. 48: 709-711, July 19, 1952; Nurs.Mirror. 95: ii-iii, July 18, 1952.
BROCKINGTON, FRASER. The health centre in Britain. Canad.J.Pub.Health. 43: 286-291, July 1952.
BROMAGE, P.R. Infected anaesthetic apparatus. (Correspondence) Brit.M.J. 2: 1042, Nov. 8, 1952.
BROOKS, C.A.S. The quality of administration, or hope for the heretic. Hospital, London. 48: 589+, Aug. 1952, Also in Canad.Hosp. 29: 80+, Nov. 1952.
BROSIN, HENRY W. Psychoanalytic training for psychiatric residents and others. Am.J.Psychiat. 109: 188-195, Sept. 1952.
BROWN, HELEN R. Ten participate in patient-centered clinic in tuberculosis nursing. Nurs.World. 126: 12-16, July 1952.
BROWN, JOHN W. Defense against biologic agents employed in warfare. Wis. M.J. 51: 584-586, June 1952.
BROWNE, HERMINA E. The use of music as a therapy. Ment.Hyg. 36: 90-103, Jan. 1952.
BROWNE, KATHERINE. Efficiency and comfort in new dining area. Canad. Hosp. 29: 32-36, June 1952.
BRUNNING, M. Physio—and occupational therapy at African hospital at Lusaka, Northern Rhodesia. Nurs.Mirror. 96: 131, Nov. 7, 1952.
BRYAN, HELEN M. Ways and means to ease the labor shortage. Hospitals. 26: 60-61, Nov. 1952.
BRYAN, JAMES E. The medical profession and Blue Shield. GP. 6: 99-103, Oct. 1952.
BRYANT, L.KATHRYN and LARSON, NANCY L. Recruiting today's nurses. Am.J.Nurs. 52: 870-871, July 1952.
BUGBEE, GEORGE. The effect of accreditation on the supply of nurses. Tex.Hosps. 8: 7+, Aug. 1952.
BUHER, WILLIAM R. Some considerations in radiation protection. (Correspondence) X-ray Technician. 24: 221+, Nov. 1952.
nurse anesthetists. J.Am.A.Nurs. Anes. 20: 255-259, Nov. 1952.
BUNDESEN, HERMAN N. Water connection to autopsy table. (Correspondence) J.A.M.A. 150: 1333, Nov. 29, 1952.
BURGOON, DAVID F. If you want good clinical laboratory service give intelligent thought to its planning and design. Mod.Hosp. 79: 102+, Oct. 1952.
BURNEY, L.E. and O'MALLEY, MARTHA. Improving health care in private and public nursing homes. Geriatrics. 7: 252+, July-Aug., 1952.
BURR, C.W. Pharmacy across Canada. Hosp.Pharm. 5: 129+, May-June 1952.
BUSINESS AND FINANCE
- Centralised hospital finance. Hosp.& Soc.Ser.J. 62: 826+, July 25, 1952.
- Financial orientation for the trustee. R.P.Sloan. Trustee. 5: 15-19, Dec. 1952.
- Financing American hospitals. R.J. Stull. R.P.A. 50: 19, Sept. 1952.
Accounting
- "A bewildering variety of figures" (Mass. governor's veto of bill to increase hospitals' reimbursement for care of indigents). (Editorial) Hospitals. 26: 81-82, Sept. 1952.
- A closer look at the accountant. H.C. Hahn. Hosp.Accounting. 6: 11-13, Oct. 1952.
- Cost accounting problems in pathology. B.Felton. Hosp.Accounting. 6: 15-16, Sept. 1952.
- Extracurricular activity for your national cash posting machine. M.S.Berkey. Hosp.Accounting. 6: 17-18, Oct. 1952.
- Hospital accounting and considerations of pharmacy operations. S.W.Martin. Hosp.Pharm. 5: 273-276, Sept.-Oct. 1952; 325-328, Sept.-Oct. 1952.
- Hospital accounts and costing - where next? J.M.Bickel. Hospital, London. 48: 687-690, Oct. 1952.
- Hospital cost accounting. S.Hodkinson. Hosp.& Health Mgt. 15: 350-352, Oct. 1952.
- Hospital costing — the next stage. W.L. Abernethy. Hosp.&Soc.Ser.J. 62: 963-964, Aug. 29, 1952; 1013-1014, Sept. 12, 1952.
- Selling top management on financial re-

Plate 8. Index of Hospital Literature.

The problem of indexing medical literature has always been of serious concern to those working in the medical field, and with the enormous growth of the periodical literature the problem has become even more serious in recent years. The difficulty encountered here is somewhat different than in the other disciplines. In the exact sciences the subject approach is the most important whereas in the subjective fields of the fine arts it is the person, *i.e.,* author or artist, who is the most important. Medicine being both an art and a science has two approaches, both the subject and the author, to its indexing problems. The solving of this problem has involved some of the best minds in the field of medicine. The beginning of scientific bibliography is usually credited to Albrecht von Haller (1708-77) whose great Bibliothecae in anatomy, surgery, medicine, and botany is the first attempt to compile an index which is both comprehensive and critical. This medical work is arranged by large subject groups and then chronologically under the subject. An alphabetical author index is included. This was the only annotated index that covered the entire field of medicine. Later indexes had to limit themselves in some way. Wilhelm Gottfried Ploucquet (1744-1814), realizing the importance of continuations, developed the cyclical or series bibliography in which new titles could be added by means of new editions or supplements each beginning where the other ended. The works of Ploucquet are arranged by subject, but unfortunately there is no author index. The next attempt to index the periodical literature of medicine was by Adolph Carl Peter Callisen (1786-1866) who compiled an author list of books and periodicals by medical writers for the period from approximately 1750 to 1830. Callisen's bibliography is limited in its usefulness, because it is only an author list and no provision was made for continuations.

This marked the end of the one man bibliographies and from then on indexing was done by a group working under the supervision of an editor, or executive, using the books and periodicals owned by one institution and published as a group project. The opportunity for a unique bibliography of the entire medical literature was afforded with the building up of the collection of the library of the Surgeon General's Office in Washington, D.C. At the close of the Civil War there were only a few volumes in the library, but with the appointment of John Shaw Billings (1838-1913) as a member of the staff, additions were made to the collection with the intent of making the library a national medical library. Billings soon realized that a library without an index was useless, so he conceived the idea of an index, the outgrowth of which gave two indexes to the medical world, the *Index-Catalogue of the Library of the Surgeon General's Office* and the *Index Medicus*. The *Index-Catalogue* is probably one of the greatest indexing projects ever undertaken in any field, and has been rightfully called one of America's greatest contributions to medical science. This publication is a combined author and subject index, arranged in dictionary form in a single alphabet. Books, pamphlets, chapters of books, and theses are listed under subject and also under author, but periodical articles are only listed under the subject. Volume one, listing all material under "A" and "B," was published in 1880; additional volumes were published until the entire alphabet was covered. This was then followed by a second series (v.1, 1896) indexing all material added since the issue of the first series. This work continued until the present fourth series (v.1, 1936) when, due to the insurmountable difficulties encountered in continuing the list, it was decided to discontinue publication with volume 11. Another index started by Billings as a private venture was the *Index Medicus*. This was a subject arranged monthly publication indexing the contents of about half of the journals, books, and pamphlets listed in the *Index-Catalogue*. Each volume has a separate author and subject index, with the exception of the third series which has only an author index.

Another bibliographic tool, the *Quarterly Cumulative*

Index to Current Medical Literature, was published from 1916 to 1926 by the American Medical Association. Twelve volumes were issued and its bound numbers are cumulative with the author and subject entries arranged alphabetically. This index is limited in scope covering only references to articles in a selected list of about 300 of the more important American and foreign medical periodicals. In 1927 the *Index Medicus* and the *Quarterly Cumulative Index* were combined to form the *Quarterly Cumulative Index Medicus.* This is a dictionary arrangement by author and subject which appears twice a year. This index includes the following information: new books listed according to author and subject, lists of medical publishers and journals indexed, and an index to the periodical literature. Titles from foreign journals appear in the original language under author and in translation only under the subject, with a few exceptions such as titles in Japanese. Titles under subject entries are frequently rearranged by key words. At present this index is about two years late in appearing which is a handicap to anyone attempting to keep abreast of the current literature.

In order to fill the gap between the appearance of the periodicals and the issuing of the *Quarterly Cumulative Index Medicus* the Armed Forces Medical Library publishes the *Current List of Medical Literature.* The issues appear monthly and are arranged by the title of the periodical indexed with each article designated by number. There is a separate subject and author index included with each issue. Reference is made to the article by means of the designated number. The indexes are cumulative in a semi-annual volume with a separate author and subject index.

Historical Indexes

Garrison and Morton, *A Medical Bibliography*

Kelly, *Encyclopedia of Medical Sources*

RESEARCH. Proceedings of the meeting of the Executive. Ottawa, No. 29, 1945–

GREAT BRITAIN. GENERAL MEDICAL COUNCIL. Address by the president at the opening of the 24th session of the General Medical Council of the United Kingdom. 19p. 8° Lond., 1877.

—— Address by the president, November 17, 1885. 8p. 8° Lond., 1885.

MOSKVA. LECHEBNOE-SANITARNOE UPRAVLENIE KREMLIA. XX let raboty lechebno-sanitarnogo upravlenia Kremlia; sbornik trudov. 393p. 27cm. Moskva, 1939.

Anders, J. M. A committee on applied medical science. Ann. Int. M., 1930, **4:** 277–80.—**Van Bastelaer.** Rapport de la Commission qui a été chargée d'examiner les travaux des Commissions médicales provinciales, année 1895 (soumis à l'Académie par M. le Ministre de l'agriculture et des travaux publics) ainsi que les observations émises par des Membres de l'Académie concernant ces travaux. Bull. Acad. méd. Belgique, 1896, 4. ser., **10:** 639–750.

—— Crisis.

See also **Civilization; Culture; Group,** Problems; **Medicine,** Problems; **Science,** Problems.

BERNHEIM, B. M. Medicine at the cross-roads. 256p. 21cm. N. Y., 1939.

BLOS, E. Die Medizin am Scheidewege; fünf Kapitel zum Aufbau einer synthetischen Medizin. 150p. 8° Karlsruhe, 1931.

GOLDSCHEIDER, J.K.A.E.A. Zeit- und Streitfragen der Heilkunst. 76p. 22cm. Lpz., 1927.

KAUP, I. Gestaltlehre des Lebens und der Rasse; Lösung der Krise in der Medizin und Hygiene. 154p. 8° Lpz., 1935.

LEONARDI, E. La crisis de la medicina. 333p. 23½cm. B. Air., 1941.

LIEK, E. G. Der Arzt und seine Sendung. 6. Aufl. 195p. 8° Münch., 1927. ALSO 10. Aufl. 254p. [1936]

—— [The same] The doctor's mission; reflections, reminiscences and revelations of a medical man; transl. by J. Ellis Barker. 276p. 12° Lond. [1930]

—— Irrwege der Chirurgie; kritische Streifzüge. 235p. 8° Münch., 1929.

—— Das Wunder in der Heilkunde. 2. Aufl. 208p. 8° Münch., 1931.

—— Die Zukünftige Entwicklung der Heilkunde. 31p. 8° Stuttg. [1931]

—— Im Bannkreis des Arztes, aus dem Nachlass. 166p. 8° Dresd., 1935.

MUCH, H. Steht die scholastische Medizin vor einem unvermeidlichen Bankerott? 35p. 12° Lpz., 1931.

OTERO, L. Bases de la crisis médica; soluciones. 221p. 26cm. B. Air., 1943.

STEHR, A. Arzt, Priesterarzt und Staatsmann. 1. Teil: Aerztliche Synthese. 2. Teil: Arzt und kranke Kultur. 111p. 8° Münch., 1933.

Aschner, B. Konstitutionstherapie als Ausweg aus der gegenwärtigen Krise der Medizin. Hippokrates, Stuttg., 1928, **1:** 41–59. —— Medicine at the crossroads. In his Art of the Healer, N. Y., 1942, 296–306.—**Bourquin, C.** La médecine officielle et la médecine. Chirurgie, Lausanne, 1944, **6:** 609–14.—**Browning, W.** Is there a medical counterpart to the Kulturgeschichte controversy? Med. Libr. Hist. J., 1905, **3:** 217–27.—**Charlin C., C.** La crisis espiritual de la medicina. Rev. med., Valparaiso, 1944–45, **18:** 265; 639. —— La crisis espiritual de la medicina de hoy. Gac. peru. cir. med., 1942–43, **5:** No. 59, 5–9.—**Cruchet, R.** La crise médicale. J. méd. Bordeaux, 1925, **55:** 827–38.—**Cushing, H.** Medicine at the cross-roads. Tr. Congr. Am. Physicians, 1933, **15:** 1–24. Also J. Am. M. Ass., 1933, **100:** 1567–75.—**Di Guglielmo, G.** La crisi della medicina nel quadro generale della cultura contemporanea. Policlinico, 1933, **40:** sez. prat., 323–9.—**Doan, C. A.** Medicine in world crisis. Ohio M. J., 1941, **37:** 321–5.—**Fries, K.** Gedanken eines Laien über die sogenannte Krise der Medizin. Aerztl. Rdsch., 1936, **46:** 10–2.—**Green, R. L.** Medicine at the crossroads. Illinois M. J., 1937, **72:** 59–63.—**Gruber, G. B.** Zur angeblichen Krisis der Medizin. Wien. klin. Wschr., 1933, **46:** 801–7.—**Haeberlin, C.** Die Heilkunde in unserer Zeitenwende. Zschr. Menschenk., 1933, **9:** 61–77.—**His, W.** Die Krise in der Medizin. Deut. Aerzte Ztg, 1932, **7:** No. 319.—**Honigmann, G.** Die Krise der Medizin in der literarischen Beleuchtung der letzten Jahre. Hippokrates, Stuttg., 1928, **1:** 170–80.—**Kraus, F.** Ueber Grundlagenkrise in der medizinischen Wissenschaft. Arch. klin. Chir., 1931, **164:** 1–4.—**Marcinowski, J.** Die Bedeutung der Weltanschauungsprobleme in der Heilkunst. Zschr. Psychother., 1909, **1:** 129–43.—**Müller, A.** Die Wende im naturwissenschaftlichen und medizinischen Denken der Gegenwart. Med. Welt, 1933, **7:** 893–5.—**Nasio, J.** Crisis médica. Día méd., B. Air., 1942, **14:** 1164.—**Neergaard, K. von.** Wandlungen der Medizin in ihren Beziehungen zur gegenwärtigen Kulturkrise. Aerztl. Sachverst. Ztg, 1934, **40:** 321–8.—**Ramsey, H. P.** Medicine at the crossroads. Med. Ann. District of Columbia, 1943, **12:** 193.—**Rees, T.** Heilkunde, Biologie und exakte Wissenschaft (Ausschnitt aus dem Schrifttum zu Fragen der Zeit) Münch. med. Wschr., 1936, **83:** 1562–4.—**Rolleston, H.** The shifting sands of the architecture of medicine. Brit. M. J., 1935, **2:** 127–9.—**Sampson, F. E.** The critical situation in medicine. Bull. Am. M. Ass., 1922–23, **16:** No. 5, 7–11.—**Schaeppi, T.** Krise und Kritiker der Medizin. Schweiz. med. Wschr., 1933, **63:** 1009–13.—**Schenck, E. G.** Wie sollen wir uns zur Schulmedizin stellen? Hippokrates, Stuttg., 1939, **10:** 1089–96.—**Siebert, F.** Der Umbruch und das Schöpferische in der Heilkunde. Oeff. Gesundhdienst, 1938–39, **4:** A, 557–68.—**Sigerist, H. E.** L'inquiétude actuelle dans le monde médical. Internat. med. W. Schweiz (1935) 1936, 1. Congr., 157–68 [Discussion] 317–27.—**Tomanek, Z.** [The medical thought in the cultural crisis] Polska gaz. lek., 1934, **13:** 493–5.—**Travagli, F.** La crisi medica nel 1934. Med. sociale, Nap., 1934, **24:** No. 9, 9–14.—**Wachholz, L.** [Decline of medicine, the crisis or the revolution?] Polska gaz. lek., 1932, **12:** 269–72.—**Wilbur, R. L.** Medicine at the cross-roads. California West. M., 1933, **38:** 337–40.

—— Criticism.

ERHARD, F. Nachdenkliches zur heutigen Heilkunde, für Laien, Aerzte und die es werden wollen. 40p. 12° Lpz., 1906.

GRAVES, B. Rational medicine; comments on social medicine, surgery and education. 291p. 22cm. Lond., 1944.

OSLER, W. Chauvinism in medicine; an address before the Canadian Medical Association, Montreal, Sept. 17, 1902. 23p. 8° Balt., 1902.

OXFORD, A. W. Masonry, medicine and morals. 41p. 16½cm. Lond., 1939.

VAN ETTEN, N. B. The quality of medicine. 2 l. 29cm. N. Y., 1939.

Also J. Indiana M. Ass., 1939, **32:** 599–603, also in Vital speeches of the day, Nov. 1, 1939.

Appleby, L. H. Quo vadis, medicina? Bull. Vancouver M. Ass., 1937–38, **14:** 155–66.—**Barker, L. F.** Manners and morals in medicine. Internat. Clin., 1929, 39. ser., **2:** 265–82.—**Barton, W. M.** Concerning the tendency to exaggeration and complexity in modern medicine. Washington M. Ann., 1911–12, **10:** 309–24.—**Braun, H.** Die Mechanisierung der Heilkunde und der praktische Arzt. Münch. med. Wschr., 1926, **73:** 27–9.—**Bryant, J. D.** The sunshine and shadow in medical endeavor. J. Am. M. Ass., 1905, **45:** 433–9.—**Burridge, W.** Some fundamental errors of medical science; a case study of overgeneralization. Papers Am. Congr. Gen. Semantics (1941) 1943, 2. Congr., 145–9.—**Buttersack.** Zur Weiterentwicklung der Heilkunst. Aerztl. Mschr., 1929, 105–7.—**Buzzard, E. F.** Arrogance and ignorance in medicine. Lancet, Lond., 1929, **2:** 695.—**Carles, J.** Le incertezze della medicina. Gazz. osped., 1934, **55:** 585–91.—**Castro Carvalho.** Medicina em travesti. Gaz. clin., S. Paulo, 1940, **38:** 96–104.—**Charlin C., C.** Los vicios de la medicina actual. Día méd., B. Air., 1943, **15:** 254–7; 1945, **17:** 137–41.—**Coole, W. A.** Medical absurdities. Messenger, 1942, **39:** No. 4, 18–22.—**Crichton-Miller, H.** The John Bull spirit in medicine. Med. J. & Rec., 1926, **124:** 1–5.—**Dalmon, H.** Sur les horizons de la médecine, le médecin moderne se profile en Janus fibron., monoculaire. Avenir méd., Par., 1938, **35:** 220–2.—**Dickinson, S. W.** Delusions in medicine. Tr. M. Soc. Virginia (1901) 1902, 19–39.—**Dorland, W. A. N.** Ex ignorantia in sapientiam: the slow growth of scientific medicine in the face of incredulity and intolerance. Chicago M. Times, 1910, **43:** 231–40.—**Ferreira, J. G.** Mecanização da medicina. Rev. méd. Paraná, 1940, **9:** 163.—**Foveau de Courmelles.** Variations biologiques, les sanctions judiciaires. J. méd. Paris, 1933, **53:** 747–9. —— Des maladies physiques: nos péchés capitaux! Ibid., 1935, **55:** 501–3. —— Les incertitudes médicales. Ibid., 1936, **56:** 193–5.—**Freeman, E. T.** Medicine from three angles. Irish J. M. Sc., 1926, 6. ser., 683–93, ch.—**Fróes, H. P.** Pelo ensino e pela medicina. Brasil med., 1940, **54:** 766–8.—**Gutiérrez, A.** Sobre los vicios de la medicina actual. Rev. méd. Hosp. españ., B. Air., 1942–43, **13:** 194; 1943, **15:** 563.—**Haggard, W. D.** By their health ye shall know them. Atlantic M. J., 1925–26, **29:** 53–5.—**Halliburton, W. D.** Knowledge and understanding. Lancet, Lond., 1921, **2:** 1139.—**Hemenway, H. B.** Uncertainties and fallacies in scientific medicine. Med. Rec., N. Y., 1905, **68:** 939–41.—**Horne, B. S.** Medical sciolism versus medical science. Proc. Indiana Eclect. M. Ass. (1905–

Plate 9. Index-Catalogue of the Library of the Surgeon General's office.

Plate 10. Quarterly Cumulative Index Medicus.

February 1954

Items 12219-12327

Section I

REGISTER OF ARTICLES

An asterisk preceding a title abbreviation indicates that one or more articles in the issue has not been indexed.

A. M. A. AMERICAN JOURNAL OF DISEASES OF CHILDREN (Chicago)

A. M. A. Am. J. Dis. Child. 86:3 Sept 53

12219 DICKINSON D G, WILSON J L, GRAHAM B D Studies in respiratory insufficiency. I. Carbon dioxide and oxygen studies in early respiratory paralysis in poliomyelitis. p. 265-72.

12220 VARGA C, WILD J Aerosol trypsin in respiratory complications of bulbar poliomyelitis; report of a case. p. 273-4.

12221 KUNSTADTER R H, GUTERMAN H S, TULSKY A S Transabdominal pneumoperitoneum as an aid in the diagnosis of sex-endocrine disturbances. p. 275-83.

12222 HOWARD P J, BAUER A R Quantitative variations in the respiration of the newborn infant. p. 284-92.

12223 BOYD G L Tuberculous pericarditis in children. p. 293-300.

12224 SABIN A B Present status and future possibilities of a vaccine for the control of poliomyelitis. p. 301-10.

12225 BELL J A Epidemiological aspects of gamma globulin prophylaxis in poliomyelitis; a critical evaluation. p. 311-8.

12226 CLIFFORD S H Postmaturity clinical syndrome and pathologic findings. p. 319-21.

12227 MILLER H C, BEHRLE F C The changing respiratory patterns in newborn infants. p. 321-2.

12228 HANSEN A E, WIESE H F Blood levels of unsaturated fatty acids as indication of nutritional requirement for essential fatty acids in children. p. 322-4.

12229 SNYDERMAN S E, PRATT E L, CHEUNG M W, HOLT E Jr, PANOS T C, HANSEN A E The minimal requirement of infants for certain amino acids. p. 324-6.

12230 KAYE R, CAUGHEY R H, McCRORY W W The minimal nitrogen requirement of infants and the effect of vitamin B12 upon it. p. 326-7.

12231 STEVENSON S S, RANOWSKI T S Some effects of thyroid or thyroxin upon premature infants. p. 327-30.

12232 HARTMANN A F Blood galactose in infants and children. p. 330-1.

12233 GARDNER L I Neutral 17-ketosteroids of plasma in children. p. 331-3.

12234 KELLEY V C, ELY R S Circulating adrenal hormones in children with endocrine and other disorders. p. 333-5.

12235 PAPADATOS C, KLEIN R Addison's diseases developing in a boy with hypoparathyroidism. p. 336-7.

12236 WILKINS L, CLAYTON G W The development of goiters in cretins without iodine deficiency. p. 337-9.

12237 JACKSON R L, RAO P T Insulin requirements from infancy to adulthood of children with diabetes mellitus in good control. p. 339-41.

12238 KAPLAN S, HELMSWORTH J A, CLARK L C Hypothermia in the diagnosis and treatment of congenital cardiovascular anomalies. p. 341-3.

12239 CALCAGNO P L, RUBIN M I, WEINTRAUB D H Diluting and concentrating mechanisms of the kidney in the premature infant. p. 344-5.

12240 YAMAZAKI J N, WRIGHT S, WRIGHT P A study of the outcome of pregnancy in women exposed to the atomic bomb in Nagasaki. p. 345-6.

12241 PREC K J, CASSELS D E Dye-dilution curves and cardiac-output determinations in newborn infants. p. 346-7.

12242 WANNAMAKER L W, DENNY F W, PERRY W D, SIEGEL A C, RAMMELKAMP C H Jr Studies on immunity to streptococcal infections in man. p. 347-8.

12243 COHLAN S Q Excessive intake of vitamin A during pregnancy as a cause of congenital anomalies in the rat. p. 348-9.

12244 WHEELER W E, WAINERMAN B The treatment and prevention of epidemic infantile diarrhea associated with Escherichia coli 0111 by the use of chloramphenicol and neomycin. p. 350-3.

12245 SCHULMAN I, SMITH C H Fetal and adult hemoglobins in premature infants with observations on the mechanism of the anemia of prematurity. p. 354-7.

A.M.A. Am. J. Dis. Child. 86:4 Oct 53

12246 BLATT N H, LEPPER M H Reactions following antirabies prophylaxis; report on sixteen patients. p. 395-402.

12247 JACKSON R L, KELLY H G, SMITH E K, WANG P, ROUTH J I Electrophoretic analyses of plasma or serum proteins of rheumatic-fever patients in relation to stages of disease. p. 403-22.

12248 LOVE W G Jr, TILLERY B New treatment for atelectasis of the newborn. p. 423-5.

12249 LUSTED L B, PICKERING D E, FISHER D, SMYTH F S Growth and metabolism in normal and thyroid-ablated infant Rhesus monkeys (Macaca mulatta). V. Roentgenographic features of skeletal development in normal and thyroid-ablated infant Rhesus monkeys (Macaca mulatta). p. 426-35.

12250 TROSSMAN C M Completely automatic Miller aerosol device. p. 436-40.

12251 AUFRANC W H National policies relative to the distribution of gamma globulin. p. 441-6.

12252 WISHIK S M Role of the general practitioner and specialist in care of physically handicapped children. p. 447-55.

12253 NADAS A S, GOODALE W T, RUDOLPH A M, BRAUDO J J Atrial septal defect. p. 456-8.

12254 GOLDBLOOM A, FERENCZ C, JOHNSON A L The problem of differential diagnosis in infants with large hearts and increased blood flow to the lungs. p. 458-60.

12255 ABELSON N M, BOGGS T R Jr Spectrophotometric absorption patterns in erythroblastosis fetalis. p. 461-2.

12256 KAPLAN E, ZUELZER W W, MOURIQUAND C The significance of visible iron in red cell precursors. p. 462-4.

12257 HSIA D Y, JONES A R, ALLEN F H Jr, GELLIS S S, DIAMOND L K Studies on erythroblastosis due to ABO incompatibility. p. 464-6.

12258 LUBCHENCO L O, BOYD E, DRESSLER M S Growth of prematurely born infants with and without retrolental fibroplasia. p. 466-8.

12259 WIXOM E, DAY E, SCHERP H, BRADFORD W L Parapertussis: observation of humoral antibodies and skin reactions to chemical fractions of the organism. p. 468-9.

12260 FABER H K, DONG L Virucidal activity of some common surface antiseptics, with special reference to poliomyelitis. p. 469-72.

12261 GOOD R A, DENNY F W, SMITH R T, THOMAS L Factors involved in the production of tissue damage by endotoxins derived from Gram-negative micro-organisms. p. 473-4.

12262 DORFMAN A, ROSEMAN S, SCHILLER S The biosynthesis of hyaluronic acid. p. 474-6.

12263 ALEXANDER H E, LEIDY G Nature of the Hemophilus influenzae cell through which heritable changes are induced by desoxyribonucleic acid. p. 475-7.

12264 SMITH M H, HOLMES B J Studies on Klebsiella and Erwinia. p. 477-8.

12265 LANGE K, SLOBODY L B, STRANG R H Prolonged intermittent corticotropin (ACTH) and cortisone therapy in the nephrotic syndrome: immunologic basis and results. p. 478-81.

12266 SMITH R T, THOMAS L The influence of age on the resistance of rabbits to the lethal effect of Gram-negative bacterial toxin. p. 481-2.

12267 KLEIN M, ZIEGLER J The role of injections as inflammatory and localizing agents. p. 482-3.

12268 WATERS W J, RICHERT D A, RAWSON H H Bilirubin encephalopathy (kernicterus). p. 483-4.

12269 WOOD S H, BUDDINGH G J A bacteriological study of acute bronchiolitis in infants. p. 485-6.

12270 ALDRICH R A, CASE J A, NEVE R A Experimental production of porphyria in the rat. p. 486-7.

12271 FELDMAN H A Congenital toxoplasmosis; a study of one hundred three cases. p. 487-9.

12272 FOMON S J, WEST C D, KAPLAN S A The contributions of filtration rate and tubular activity to the control of electrolyte excretion. p. 489-91.

12273 KLEIN R, FORTUNATO J, PAPADATOS C Circulating adrenal hormone in children in health and disease. p. 491-4.

12274 HENNESSY A V, MINUSE E, DAVENPORT F M, FRANCIS T Jr An experience with vaccination against influenza B in 1952 using monovalent vaccine. p. 494.

12275 SARETT H P, SNIPPER L P The comparative effects of fructose and glucose in the diet of alloxan-diabetic rats. p. 494-6.

12276 WEST J R, DI SANT'AGNESE P A Studies of pulmonary function in cystic fibrosis of the pancreas. p. 496-8.

12277 FELTON H M Clinical trial of a soluble pertussis antigen. p. 499-500.

12278 OSBORN J J Prolonged interruption of the circulation at extremely low body temperatures in dogs; an experimental surgical procedure. p. 500-2.

12279 CONWAY D J Capillary permeability to plasma albumin and gamma globulin. p. 502-3.

12280 LOWE C U, WILLIAMS W L The effect of cortisone upon certain protein-nucleic acid components of liver cells. p. 503-5.

12281 HSIA D Y, GOLDBLOOM R B, GELLIS S S Studies on the relation of mechanical fragility of erythrocytes to physiological jaundice. p. 505-9.

12282 STEIGMAN A J H, KOKKO U P, SILVERBERG R J Unusual properties of a virus isolated from the spinal cord of a child with fatal poliomyelitis. p. 509-10.

12283 GRIBETZ D, TALBOT N B, CRAWFORD J D Observations on six children with goiter due to chronic lymphocytic thyroiditis. p. 510-1.

12284 BRUCK E Renal function in anemia. p. 511-2.

12285 KUNZ H W, MELLIN G W, CHEUNG M W, PRATT E L Impairment of urinary concentration in sickle-cell anemia. p. 512.

12286 McCRORY W W, GOREN N GORNFELD D Demonstration of impairment of urinary concentration ability, or pitressin-resistance, in children with sickle-cell anemia. p. 512-5.

A. M. A. ARCHIVES OF DERMATOLOGY AND SYPHILOLOGY (Chicago)

A.M.A. Arch. Derm. Syph. 68:4 Oct 53

12287 KLAUDER J V Sherlock Holmes as a dermatologist, with remarks on the life of Dr. Joseph Bell and the Sherlockian method of teaching. p. 363-77.

12288 ADONI L Streptomycin in treatment of cutaneous tuberculosis. p. 378-81.

12289 ZELIGMAN I, SINESI S J Carbuncle caused by Gaffkya tetragena treated with oxytetracycline (terramycin). p. 382-4.

12290 HUFF S E, TAYLOR H L Observations on peripheral circulation in psoriasis. p. 385-8.

12291 KURTIN A Corrective surgical planing of skin; new technique for treatment of acne scars and other skin defects. p. 389-97.

12292 ROSENBERG W A Multiple superficial epitheliomatosis; spectroscopic study. p. 398-401.

12293 GRAIS M L Role of colloidal oatmeal in dermatologic treatment of the aged. p. 402-7.

12294 TELOH H A Correlation of rate of growth with histologic characteristics of basal cell carcinoma. p. 408-16.

12295 APPEL B, BALER G R, DOUGHERTY E F Isoniazid in the treatment of chronic lupus erythematosus. p. 417-20.

12296 NEUMANN A Pseudoainhum; report of congenital case involving several fingers and left wrist. p. 421-7.

12297 ROBINSON H M Jr, FIGGE F H, BERESTON E S Inhibition of tyrosin-tyrosinase reaction by Microsporum audouini; preliminary report. p. 428-9.

12298 SHELLEY W B, HURLEY H J Jr, NICHOLS A C Axillary odor; experimental study of the role of bacteria, apocrine sweat, and deodorants. p. 430-46.

12299 ORFUSS A J Lymphocytic infiltration of the skin. p. 447-9.

12300 FISHER A A Herpes gestationis (Rh-positive, type O) treated with cortisone and progesterone. p. 449-51.

12301 SULZBERGER M B The present status of hydrocortisone acetate ointment in dermatologic therapy. p. 451-2.

12302 REIN C R The present status of hydrocortisone acetate ointment in dermatologic therapy. p. 452-6.

12303 WELLS G C Postinflammatory hyperpigmentation. p. 459.

12304 KLAK W, LORINCZ A L Case for diagnosis (reticulated melanosis?). p. 459-61.

12305 BUCHHOLZ A M Papular myxedema (papular mucinosis.). p. 461-2.

12306 DIRECTOR W, LYSIAK R Leprosy, lepromatous type: response to isoniazid therapy. p. 463.

12307 WOLF J, BRAITMAN M Tuberculoid leprosy. p. 463-4.

12308 ORFUSS A J, ROBBINS S Epitheliomata, multiple, basal-cell type, of the face and forehead treated with thorium X. p. 464-5.

12309 WOLF J, APPELL H S Case for diagnosis: xeroderma pigmentosum? p. 466-8.

12310 SOBEL N, KLEEBERG L S Case for diagnosis: linear lichenoid purpuric dermatosis? p. 468-9.

12311 DIRECTOR W, ROGACHEFSKY H Pemphigus folicaceus: response to corticotropin (ACTH) and cortisone; appearance of acanthotic lesions. p. 469-70.

12312 TOLMACH J A Case for diagnosis. p. 470-1.

12313 SAMITZ M H, SATANOVE A, KIRSHBAUM B Subacute disseminated lupus erythematosus. p. 471-2.

12314 SAMITZ M H, SATANOVE A, KIRSHBAUM B Sarcoidosis involving the mucous membranes. p. 473-4.

12315 SAMITZ M H, SATANOVE A, KIRSHBAUM B Sarcoidosis treated with quinacrine hudrochloride (atabrine dihydrochloride). p. 472-3.

12316 KLAUDER J V Sarcoid of the eyelids, conjunctiva, and uveal tract treated with quinacrine hydrochloride (atabrine dihydrochloride). p. 474.

12317 BUTTERWORTH T Hapalonychia. p. 474-5.

12318 NEW W M, HORTON S H Multiple acanthoma (tumor-like keratosis of Poth) p. 475-8.

A. M. A. Arch. Derm. Syph. 68:5 Nov 53

12319 BRENNAN J G Contributions to the study of pemphigus. p. 481-98.

12320 ALLISON S D Psychosomatic dermatology circa 1850. p. 499-502.

12321 BYERS J L, BRADLEY D F Primary pustular gonorrhea of the skin. p. 503-5.

12322 McLAUGHLIN J T, SHOEMAKER R J, GUY W B Personality factors in adult atopic eczema. p. 506-16.

12323 GAUL L E Heredity of multiple benign cystic epithelioma: The Indiana family. p. 517-24.

12324 VOLLMER H Treatment of eczema with cortisone ointment. p. 525-9.

12325 BENJAMIN F B, CORNBLEET T Influence of local factors on cutaneous injury and healing. p. 530-5.

12326 CORMIA F E, COSTELLO M J, BARKER L P, NELSON C T, WILSON E W, CRAMER J A Isoniazid (nydrazid) in treatment of cutaneous diseases: Cutaneous tuberculosis, leprosy, sarcoidosis, and miscellaneous dermatoses. p. 536-44.

12327 BUTTERWORTH T Influence of pressure on nodules of xanthoma tuberosum. p. 545-8.

187

Plate 11. Current List of Medical Literature.

Other types of bibliographic reference tools are those works which give historical sources. Garrison and Morton's *Medical Bibliography* is a check list of texts illustrating the history of medical sciences, and serves as a valuable aid in checking bibliographic items. The arrangement is by special subject fields with the literature chronological under each subject. Most of the entries are annotated which is a distinct contribution. There is a separate personal name and subject index. Kelly's *Encyclopedia* lists the "earliest or best" articles or books on medical discoveries and practices arranged alphabetically by the name of the author with a subject index. Information includes author, dates, an identifying phrase, statement of subject, and references in full to sources of article.

Cumulative Indexes

American Journal of Physiology
Journal of Physiology
Journal of Biological Chemistry
Journal of Bacteriology
Cancer Research
Medical Clinics of North America
Surgical Clinics of North America
Surgery, Gynecology and Obstetrics
American Journal of Nursing
National League of Nursing Education. Annual Reports
Annals of Medical History
Bulletin of the History of Medicine

In addition to the periodical indexes, a number of periodicals compile cumulative indexes which are issued at regular or irregular intervals of time. Most of these indexes are arranged separately by author and subject. The *American Journal of Physiology* has issued three indexes, the last two at 30 volume intervals. The *Journal of Physiology* has also issued three indexes at irregular volume intervals. The indexes to the *Journal of Biological Chemistry* have appeared at 25 volume intervals. Two indexes covering volumes 1-30, and 31-64 have been issued by the *Journal of Bacteriology*. *Cancer Research* published a decennial author and subject index covering its first 10 years. The various medical specialties are also represented in the

Plate 12. Cumulative Index of the American Journal of Nursing.

cumulative indexes. The *Medical Clinics of North America* and the *Surgical Clinics of North America* issue subject indexes every third year. *Surgery, Gynecology and Obstetrics* has two indexes appearing at 40 volume intervals. The *American Journal of Nursing* is presently issuing indexes for 5 year periods instead of 10 year intervals. The index to the *Annual Reports of the National League of Nursing Education* appeared in two numbers. The first issue covered a 45 year period and the second 10 years. The *Annals of Medical History* published an index to its entire set arranging the material in dictionary form for authors and subjects. The *Bulletin of the History of Medicine* issued a separate author and subject index to its first 20 volumes.

Abstract Journals

Biological Abstracts
Chemical Abstracts
Federation Proceedings
Abstracts of World Medicine
Excerpta Medica
Obstetrical and Gynecological Survey
International Medical Digest
International Surgical Digest
International Abstracts of Surgery
Nutrition Abstracts and Reviews
Cancer Current Literature
Diabetes Abstracts
Ophthalmic Literature
Tuberculosis Index
Dental Abstracts
Nuclear Science Abstracts
Psychological Abstracts

The continued growth of the periodical literature resulted in the development of a new kind of index, the abstract journal. The abstract journal summarizes articles which have appeared in other journals. This is a great help in enabling one to keep track of all pertinent information being published in a particular field. The most successful abstract journals were the German publications prior to the first World War. After the war they ceased to exist and only recently the English language journals have come into prominence. The interdependence of scientists in all fields has necessitated a more adequate coverage of the literature. In addition to the strictly abstract journals many journals have sections devoted to abstracts. Abstract journals are issued in many fields. The basic sciences such as biology and chemistry are covered, many of the medical specialties, and some diseases such as cancer and tuberculosis. The first three journals listed are those that abstract articles in the basic sciences. *Biological Abstracts* abstracts journal articles in the fields of theoretical and applied biology. Twelve numbers with an author and subject index comprise a volume. Indexes are arranged by author, subject, systematic, geographical, and geological divisions. The journal is divided into five sections representing the fields of general biology; basic medical sciences; microbiology, immunology, public health, and parasitology; plant sciences; and animal sciences. *Chemical Abstracts* is now the most comprehensive of the abstract journals. There is an author index with each semi-monthly issue and an annual author, subject, and formula index. Decennial indexes have been issued in 1916, 1926, 1936, and 1946. *Chemical Abstracts* has a wide coverage of all phases of chemistry and related sciences, such as physics, mathematics, biology, and physiology. The short delay following the appearance of the original article and the excellent indexing makes it one of the most useful of the scientific and technical journals. *Federation Proceedings* abstracts papers presented before the annual meeting of the Federation of American Societies for Experimental Biology and Medicine. An author index of the papers abstracted is included. In addition original papers are published as well as a list of members, society proceedings, constitution and by-laws, and other items regarding the activities of the societies. There is a general index to each volume.

The next group of abstract journals represents the clinical specialties. *Abstracts of World Medicine* abstracts selective articles under broad classification. All abstracts are in English and with each issue there is a separate author and subject index. The *Excerpta Medica* is the most ambitious attempt ever undertaken to abstract in the English language every article in every available medical journal in the world. There are 17 sections issued monthly covering the different fields of medicine. Within these sections the articles are arranged according to a broad classification scheme. An alphabetical author index appears with each issue. An author and subject index for each volume is also issued. The *Obstetrical and Gynecological Survey* is an excellent journal. There is an international coverage of the literature and the abstracts are so complete that the original sources do not usually have to be consulted. An author index is included with each issue and a separate author and subject index with each annual volume. The *International Medical Digest* and the *International Surgical Digest* appear monthly, are not comprehensive, and do not cover much foreign literature. They are of particular interest to the general practitioner. The *International Abstracts of Surgery* issued as a supplement to *Surgery, Gynecology and Obstetrics* is an important source of surgical literature. A separate subject and author index appears with each volume.

A number of abstract journals covering special subjects or diseases are issued. *Nutrition Abstracts and Reviews* is a comprehensive abstract journal covering the chemistry of foods, physiology of nutrition, diet in health and disease, vitamins, deficiency diseases, and the feeding of animals. An author and subject index appears with each annual volume. *Cancer Current Literature,* although not an abstract journal in the sense that the others are, does serve as a bibliographic record of articles in the cancer field. Foreign titles are translated into English and reference is made to abstracts appearing in other journals. The issues appear monthly having a subject arrangement with an author index. A policy in regard to issuing cumulative indexes has apparently not been established since the practice has varied in the past. *Diabetes Abstracts* is a quarterly abstract journal covering all aspects of diabetes. It ceased publication with the 1951 volume. At that time a separate author and subject index was issued covering the last five years. The abstracts have been continued in the abstract section of the new journal *Diabetes*. *Ophthalmic Literature* is a valuable abstract journal which presents abstracts under various groupings. There are review sections with bibliographies. An annual subject and author index is issued with each volume. The *Tuberculosis Index* is an international coverage of articles relating to all phases of tuberculosis. There is a subject arrangement of the material with brief abstracts. Many articles are only cited. Since 1952 an author index has appeared with each quarterly issue in addition to the annual author index. *Dental Abstracts* is becoming a very valuable tool to those desiring information on dental material. Many foreign journals not indexed elsewhere are included in this work. The material is arranged by broad subject classification. There is no author or subject index. *Nuclear Science Abstracts* covers the literature of nuclear science and engineering. It includes not only the reports of the Atomic Energy Commission, but also material in technical and scientific journals, and unpublished research reports of government agencies, universities, and industrial research establishments. A separate author and subject index, and a numerical index of reports is issued every quarter cumulating at the end of 6 and 12 months. *Psychological Abstracts* is an important abstracting tool of the literature in the field of psychology. It appears monthly listing new books and articles grouped by subjects. There is an author index with each number and full author and subject indexes for each volume.

CHAPTER 5

THE PERIODICAL COLLECTION

MEDICAL PERIODICALS are the most important part of the library's collection. A medical library is somewhat different from other libraries where the emphasis is largely on books. There is a reason for this. Medical science is progressing so rapidly that only by a current periodical literature is one able to keep abreast of the times. It is not stretching the truth too much to say that as soon as a book is published it is out of date. Then, too, books, as a rule do not contain original material; they are more in the nature of reviews. Periodicals are published weekly, semi-monthly, monthly, bi-monthly, or quarterly. Scientific and medical societies in some cases publish their proceedings in an annual volume. Recently the annual periodical bound as a book has become very popular. Early in the history of scientific periodicals the term journal was used since these periodicals were often sponsored by a scientific or medical society and became the means by which the society published its proceedings. Certain practices developed in designating journals. They are numbered by volumes on a yearly or semi-yearly basis as a rule. Individual monthly or weekly issues are numbered also. The paging is by volume. Therefore it is the practice to refer to an article by volume, and sometimes by number of issue, page or paging, and date. At the completion of a volume it is customary to bind it in book form. If the volume is small more than one volume may be bound together.

Medical periodical literature has had an enormous growth. In this country alone over 500 medical periodicals are being issued. At present in the *World List of Scientific Periodicals,* covering the period from 1900 to 1950, approximately 50,000 journals are listed and of this number at least 5,000 are medical. Medical libraries are further burdened by the outstanding contributions that are being made to medical science by chemists, physicists, biologists, and the social scientists. As these contributions are being published in other than strictly medical journals, the duty of subscribing to and building up files of many border line journals has become almost a necessity. The journals available in a medical library lend themselves to certain arbitrary grouping. They range all the way from highly scholarly and technical journals to the more semi-popular type. All of the basic sciences of medicine, medical specialties, dentistry, hospital, and nursing are represented. A few examples of each type will be given with a brief discussion.

General Science Journals

Nature
Science
Scientific American
Scientific Monthly

Nature and *Science* are the most scholarly scientific journals published. *Scientific American* and *Scientific Monthly* do not as a rule report results of experimental research. Their articles are based on reports from the literature and are written in a more or less popular style.

Basic Science Journals

American Journal of Anatomy
Anatomical Record
Journal of Anatomy
Journal of Bacteriology
Biochemical Journal
Journal of Biological Chemistry
Society of Experimental Biology and Medicine. Proceedings
A.M.A. Archives of Pathology
American Journal of Pathology

Journal of Pathology and Bacteriology
American Journal of Physiology
Journal of Physiology

All of these journals publish original articles in their fields, and in most cases are the official organs of their respective societies. They vary in the type of indexing for each volume. Some have a dictionary arrangement for author and subject, others a separate index, and still others only a table of contents.

General Medical Journals

American Medical Association. Journal
British Medical Journal
Lancet
American Practitioner and Digest of Treatment
GP
Canadian Medical Association Journal
New England Journal of Medicine
Southern Medical Journal
California Medicine
Minnesota Medicine

The general medical journals constitute quite a large group. They are usually the official organ of a national or regional society, and their articles are written for the general practitioner. In addition to medical information they contain information of general interest to the profession. The *Journal of the American Medical Association* is the official organ of the American Medical Association. The journal appears weekly and contains original articles, clinical notes, reports from the various councils, news of interest to the profession, abstracts from the literature, book reviews, and reports of the organization. A separate subject and author index is published at the end of each volume. Book notices, deaths, medico-legal abstracts, and societies are indexed under these titles. An asterisk preceding the page number in the subject index indicates an original article in the *Journal.* In the author index an asterisk preceding the page reference indicates the article has been published in full in the *Journal.* The *British Medical Journal* is the British equivalent of the *Journal of the American Medical Association.* The index is a dictionary arranged author and subject index. Subject entries for original articles, leading articles, annotations, and correspondence are indicated by the use of symbols (O), (L), (A), and (C), respectively. The *Lancet* is the oldest extant medical journal published in the world and one of the best journals in the field. *American Practitioner* and *GP* are examples of journals written for the general practitioner. The *Canadian Medical Association Journal* is the official organ of the Canadian Medical Association and its contents are similar to the other national journals. The remaining journals mentioned are examples of regional and state society publications. They vary of course in the quality of the material published.

Clinical Specialty Journals

Anesthesiology
British Journal of Anaesthesia
A.M.A. Archives of Dermatology
British Journal of Dermatology and Syphilis
American Journal of Obstetrics and Gynecology
Journal of Obstetrics and Gynaecology of the British Empire
A.M.A. Archives of Internal Medicine
Annals of Internal Medicine
A.M.A. Archives of Ophthalmology
British Journal of Ophthalmology
A.M.A. Archives of Otolaryngology
Annals of Otology, Rhinology, and Laryngology
American Journal of Psychiatry
Brain
Journal of Bone and Joint Surgery

Journal of Pharmacology and Experimental Therapeutics
British Journal of Pharmacology and Chemotherapy
A.M.A. American Journal of Diseases of Children
Pediatrics
Archives of Physical Medicine and Rehabilitation
British Journal of Physical Medicine
American Journal of Public Health and the Nation's Health
American Journal of Roentgenology, Radium Therapy and Nuclear Medicine
British Journal of Radiology
Annals of Surgery
British Journal of Surgery
Surgery, Gynecology and Obstetrics
Journal of Urology
British Journal of Urology

The clinical specialties are well represented; anesthesiology, dermatology, gynecology and obstetrics, internal medicine, ophthalmology, otolaryngology, neurology and psychiatry, orthopedics, pharmacology, pediatrics, physical medicine, preventive medicine, radiology, surgery, and urology all have their journals. The contents of these journals are rather similar. They contain original articles, abstracts, book reviews, and news of interest to the profession. The policy in regard to the indexes varies. The most popular type of index is a separate one for author and subject. Most of the A.M.A. journals have adopted the policy of subject entries for all articles with an asterisk placed before all original articles. Author entries are made for original articles and society transactions. Book reviews and society transactions are indexed under those headings in their alphabetical order under the letters "B" and "S," respectively.

Dental Journals

American College of Dentists. Journal
American Dental Association. Journal

American Journal of Orthodontics
British Dental Journal
Journal of Dental Research
Journal of Periodontology
Oral Surgery, Oral Medicine and Oral Pathology

The material in these journals is similar to the other professional journals. The journals of the large professional societies are indexed in the *Quarterly Cumulative Index Medicus* and in some instances in the *Current List of Medical Literature.*

Review Journals

Bacteriological Reviews
Biological Reviews
Chemical Reviews
Medicine
Physiological Reviews
Quarterly Review of Biology
Annual Review of Biochemistry
Annual Review of Physiology
Annual Review of Medicine
Progress in Neurology and Psychiatry
Progress in Organic Chemistry
Advances in Biological and Medical Physics
Advances in Carbohydrate Chemistry
Advances in Internal Medicine
Advances in Pediatrics
Year Book of Dentistry
Year Book of General Surgery
Year Book of Medicine
Year Book of Obstetrics and Gynecology
Year Book of Pediatrics

At the present time there are many types of review journals being published under various titles and treating the subject matter somewhat differently. The first six journals listed are critical surveys of the work being done in various subject fields. Their chief value lies in their comprehensive coverage of a topic, including the historical background, experimental work being carried out, results obtained, and the present status of the investigation. The articles are usually followed by exhaustive lists of references and are very valuable from a bibliographic standpoint. The Annual Review and Progress In review the contemporary literature and are written by authors with a special knowledge of the subject. The same general subjects are reported on every year. Progress In is similar to the Annual Review but treats the material in a more scholarly manner. Advances In are personalized monographs of contemporary interest. The topics are diversified and timely; the reviews are comprehensive and the authors are recognized authorities in their fields. These periodicals are published both in the basic sciences as well as the clinical specialties and are indexed with a separate author and subject index. The yearbooks cover the clinical specialties. They discuss the literature under broad headings and serve as a running commentary of the pertinent literature published in the field. The material is indexed under author and subject.

History of Medicine Journals

Bulletin of the History of Medicine	*Annals of the History of Medicine*
Isis	*Ciba Symposia*
Journal of the History of Medicine and Allied Sciences	*Medical Life*

The journals in the first column are those journals which are being published today in the history of medicine and science. Those in the second column are not published at present but contain excellent articles. Articles on the history of medicine are also published in the other professional journals.

Hospital Journals

Hospitals
Hospital Management
Hospital Progress
Modern Hospital
Guy's Hospital Gazette
Guy's Hospital Reports
Harper Hospital Bulletin
Hospital for Joint Diseases. Bulletin
Johns Hopkins Hospital. Bulletin
Mount Sinai Hospital. Journal

The first four journals in this group contain articles on hospital administration and procedures. Their indexes are arranged in dictionary form for author and subject. The remaining journals are those published by the hospitals themselves. They contain reports of original investigations, case reports, book reviews, news of interest to their staff, and are indexed in dictionary form for author and subject.

Nursing Journals

American Journal of Nursing
California State Nurses Association. Bulletin
Canadian Nurse
Nursing Outlook
Nursing Research
Nursing Times
Nursing World

These journals publish articles of interest to the nursing profession. They are organized on a pattern similar to the other professional journals. Their indexes are arranged in dictionary form for author and subject.

Part III

Methods of Bibliography

CHAPTER 1

PRINCIPLES OF SCIENTIFIC INVESTIGATION

THIS SECTION of the text deals with the reference paper. Since the writing of such a paper is a scientific procedure a brief résumé is herewith presented of what science is and what some of the distinguishing features of the scientific method are. Science, according to any dictionary, is organized knowledge. But science is more than organized knowledge. It is also a method of investigating nature. There are only three processes in any scientific investigation, namely, the choosing of facts, the formation of a hypothesis that links them together, and the testing of the hypothesis by observation. A hypothesis is the first guess or a tentative assumption to explain the relationship of the observed facts. A simple hypothesis may be a mere generalization of the observations. The testing of the hypothesis consists of deducing certain consequences that would follow if the hypothesis is the correct one. These consequences may be tested by subjecting them to empirical tests or searching for additional facts or examples. When the consequences have been subjected to repeated tests and the same result is forthcoming the hypothesis is valid and a new "scientific" discovery is said to have been made. The sciences are grouped into two classes, those dealing with nature's laws or the natural sciences, and those dealing with the social activities of man or the social sciences. The methods of investigation for both are the same. The principal differences are the instruments of measurement which make for greater accuracy in the results obtained in the natural sciences. Then, too, the natural sciences lend themselves more easily to the control of variables in conducting experiments.

There are several distinguishing features of the scientific method. The first is observed facts. All scientific thinking is based on facts assembled by observation. The simplest method in the solving of any problem is to "look and see." The second feature is the employment of analysis and synthesis. Natural phenomena are complex. Also, man's ability to percieve and comprehend is limited. Problems are best understood by breaking them down into their component parts, identifying each element, and then studying their interrelationships in order to determine the factors that bind them together in the total situation. The third feature is the use of the hypothesis in guiding the thinking process. In this process a hypothesis or generalization is advanced to explain tentatively the relationship between facts. As the investigation proceeds, one hypothesis is discarded in favor of another. Several hypotheses may be tested before one is found which, under repeated tests, explains the relation between the assembled facts. The fourth feature is the verification of the consequences of the hypothesis by inference, observation, and controlled observation (experiment). It is in this phase of the scientific method that the various sciences differ, since their instruments of measurement vary so widely. The fifth feature is the use of quantitative methods in the treatment of data. There is little guess work in the treatment of scientific data. The results of measurements must be organized in comparable units to make the analysis, classification, and summarization of data more reliable. The sixth feature is judgment. There is no place in scientific investigation for a subjective approach. One's judgment must be unprejudiced and impersonal. A scientist must show great mental energy, be apt in drawing inferences, ingenious in making hypotheses, and, of course, logical in his reasoning.

Science employs several methods or procedures in interpreting data for the solving of problems or in verifying hypotheses. Among these may be mentioned the normative-survey method. In this case the situation under investigation may be surveyed, tested, and described interpretatively in terms of all obtainable facts and, in particular, with reference to norms. This type of research attempts to interpret the present by abstracting whatever generalization is possible from current experiences. Another procedure is the historical method. Historical research deals with past experiences. Its problem is to apply the method of reflective thinking to social problems by investigation of past trends of events, facts, or attitudes. A third procedure is the experimental method. The experimental attitude is basic in the thinking of scientists in the natural and social sciences. An open mind and a willingness to try and see what happens is essential to this method. Observation merges into experiment when an experimental factor acts so that the hypothesis may be tested in terms of variables. It is by repeated empirical observations that the validity of conclusions are tested and proven. A number of other procedures have been worked out in later years, a description of which may be obtained from the recommended readings. Practically all these procedures involve the bibliographic approach, which is the technique employed in assembling facts from the literature and the presentation of these facts in an interpretive manner. When scientific literature was comparatively small it probably was a simple task in an adequate library to compile all the facts in the literature pertaining to any subject under investigation, but as scientific literature continued to grow, it became necessary to develop certain skills and techniques in order to assemble the facts as recorded in the literature. This, too, has developed into an art necessitating some training. The various bibliographic tools have been described previously. The remaining chapters will be devoted to the utilization of these tools.

CHAPTER 2

THE REFERENCE PAPER

THE REFERENCE paper is a report of an investigation or problem in which the material or facts are largely drawn from the literature. The paper itself may be one of several forms depending on its purpose. The essay type is usually for a class presentation or address. A review paper surveys the literature of a given subject. The report of an investigation gives the findings of others as well as your own in some research project. Preparing a reference paper is good training in acquiring information from the ideas of others, locating this material, selecting pertinent data, and presenting it in a logical form. Such papers give training in the writing process. The composition or the scholarly report all require the same procedures, namely, selection of a subject to investigate, the gathering and selecting of material, planning of the discussion, the results, summary or conclusion, and, finally, organization of the footnotes and bibliography.

THE SUBJECT AND THE WORKING BIBLIOGRAPHY

The first problem confronting the student is the selection of a subject, and the preparation of the working bibliography. This requires some thinking about a topic or topics and some preliminary reading. The best approach is to select a subject in which you are interested. Avoid a topic which is too general, as, for example, the history of medicine in the United States or communicable disease nursing. Such topics are beyond the scope of a subject to be treated in a paper from two to three thousand words. A research worker in medicine does not try to discover the causal factor of all diseases, but segregates the problem into one very small phase. By this method he hopes to make some contribution to its understanding so that eventually, after many workers have contributed to the problem, a solution may be found. Learn to limit your topic. You may limit it by area, time, subject, person, and many other items. Do not select a topic in which all the factual information is too well known, as, for example, "What led up to the 1937 issue of a *Curriculum Guide for Schools of Nursing?*" In this case all of the information is given in the introduction to the *Guide*. The bridging of the gap, from what is known and what we would like to know, is usually accomplished by employing the hypothesis, which has been discussed previously. Frequently the contributions made by the leaders in your chosen profession make interesting subjects for investigation. The work of Dr. Trudeau at Saranac Lake should prove of interest, and if you wish to do something original why not investigate the influence his treatment of tuberculosis had in this country and, particularly, in your own area. Another factor to be considered in selecting a subject is whether the sources you are likely to use are present in the library. It is of little use to select a topic and find the material is not available. A good policy to follow is to select tentatively several subjects to investigate, and, after some preliminary reading, a problem will present itself.

After you have selected a subject or tentative subject, the next procedure is to begin compiling the working bibliography. This bibliography should be kept on standard 4 by 6 cards and should include the source of the reference and a brief comment of the subject content of the book or article for future reference. It is much easier to record all bibliographic information as you examine the reference the first time. If you do not, it will mean referring to the reference again with the resultant loss of time. This can be very inconvenient if the source is in another library, necessitating a special trip to examine it. The cards should be filed alphabetically by author and numbered for future reference. On this card the comments regarding the contents should be brief. For example, a book by Lawrason Brown, *The Story of Clinical Pulmonary Tuberculosis,* could have this brief notation: "Describes the four periods in the history of tuberculosis, giving diagnoses and treatment, including many of the classical writings." Annotations should be brief. Avoid repetitions of "this book," "the article," "this report," and such phrases. Active verbs used at the beginning of an annotation can show different shades of meaning.

THE TENTATIVE OUTLINE

From your preliminary reading and the preparation of the working bibliography you should have sufficient knowledge of what you propose to investigate to be able to prepare a tentative outline. The outline should consist of the title of your paper followed by a statement of the purpose or objectives, definitions of terms, and then the main divisions and sub-divisions so far as you are able to determine from your readings at this point. The tentative outline may be presented either as a series of questions or topics. A good approach to the problem is to jot down as many questions as you can. Do not try at first to arrange the questions in a logical order. Later these questions can be arranged in the form of an outline. If you have selected as a subject the investigation of tuberculosis control in the Lower Mississippi Valley, the title would be as follows: What has been the development of tuberculosis control in the Lower Mississippi Valley? This could also serve as your objective or purpose or you may wish to formulate a question that limits the problem to a more specific study of the sanatorium movement. The outline would then be:

I. What were the trends in tuberculosis control in the Lower Mississippi Valley leading up to and including the inauguration of the sanatorium movement? (Statement of the problem.)

II. What is meant by tuberculosis control? What area is included in the Lower Mississippi Valley? What is meant by sanatorium treatment?

III. What are the sources or possible sources of information?

IV. Into what four periods does Osler divide the history of tuberculosis?

V. What were some of the early treatments of tuberculosis in the Lower Mississippi Valley?

VI. What were some of the methods of treatment at the beginning of the modern era?

VII. What was the contribution to tuberculosis control made by Dr. Edward Livingston Trudeau?

VIII. What was the contribution to tuberculosis control made by Dr. Wallace Joseph Durel?

IX. What can you conclude from this study?

If you prefer to develop a topic outline it can very easily be done as follows:

The Development of Tuberculosis Control
in the Lower Mississippi Valley

To study the trends in tuberculosis control in the Lower Mississippi Valley, particularly the development of the sanatorium movement as inaugurated in this country by Dr. Edward Livingston Trudeau.

I. Definitions of terms:

A. Tuberculosis control.

B. Lower Mississippi Valley.
C. Sanitorium treatment.

II. Four periods in the history of tuberculosis (Osler's description):
A. Dawn of history to middle of 17th century.
B. Middle of 17th through 18th century.
C. First three quarters of the 19th century.
D. c.1864-1869 to 1882.

III. First descriptions and early treatment in the Lower Mississippi Valley:
A. By a Dr. Hall.
B. By Dr. Samuel A. Cartwright.

IV. Beginnings of the Modern Era:
A. Importance of the year 1882.
B. "Bacillus" period.
C. Other methods of treatment.

V. Sanatorium Era:
A. Contributions of Dr. Edward Livingston Trudeau.
B. Contributions of Dr. Wallace Joseph Durel to the Sanatorium movement in the Lower Mississippi Valley.

VI. Summary and conclusions.

The tentative outline is a guide to the material you hope to find from your sources. It will enable you to summarize what has been found and what additional information you will need.

PROCEDURES IN SEARCHING

It is obvious that procedures in searching begin when you are trying to select a subject to study. In your preliminary readings you should consult the general works, such as encyclopedias. There are general encyclopedias, medical encyclopedias, and special encyclopedias for the more specialized fields in history, education, and the other social sciences. Resort may have to be made to the dictionary in order to obtain an understanding of the terminology involved and the meaning of certain terms that will be used to state your problem. The next procedure is acquiring a more detailed knowledge. Books and handbooks in the various sciences serve this purpose. Books published on the subject can be found listed in the book catalogs and the card catalog of the library. The latter of course will serve another purpose in advising you of the titles that are available. This is very important as mentioned previously. Attempting to obtain titles that are not in the library or a local library can be a great handicap, although essential titles can be borrowed through interlibrary loan. Handbooks are published in most of the sciences although many are foreign language publications.

Books, however, do not bring the subject up to date and for that reason it is best to search for a survey or a review article. The various review journals will serve this purpose; their coverage has been discussed previously. They serve the additional purpose of having extensive bibliographies which will guide you to other sources of information. This is true of most of the material you read, so be careful in noting references in the literature to other sources. Most of the medical sciences and allied fields have the review type of publication. Abstract journals are another tool to be consulted. They serve not only as bibliographic sources but their abstracts serve as a guide to the contents of the article. By this time you have your tentative outline and can eliminate articles that will not serve your particular purpose. Special bibliographies should be consulted if there are any in the field you are interested in. Good examples of these are the bibliographies on infantile paralysis and on nursing. The next step is the reading of the current journal articles. The latest articles have not been abstracted so it becomes necessary to read the originals. At this stage the student has become familiar with the workers in the field and, also, the journals which are likely to contain articles on the subject. Consult the various periodical indexes which have already been listed. The student should also examine the cumulative indexes of the journals which are likely to have articles on the desired subject. These indexes are more likely to index thoroughly and in greater detail the material in their journals than the periodical indexes.

The student should not forget the authority, or the well-informed person, in the field under investigation. Consult such persons, if available, as they are more than likely to guide you to current material that has not yet been indexed, or to ephemeral sources. Other sources that may be consulted are the indexes to public documents, newspapers, hospital, institution, and society reports, to mention a few.

In searching the literature there is never any assurance that all the possible sources have been consulted. None of the indexes or bibliographies are complete in themselves. There are always gaps. For that reason consult all the indexes that may cover your subject. A vital piece of data may be listed in one and not the other. You will in most cases proceed from the more general works to the specific which in this case is from the encyclopedias and books to the review and abstract journals, and the specialized indexes and bibliographies. The next step in your procedure is the taking of notes from the various sources you have consulted.

NOTE TAKING

The student is now in a position to begin a more detailed note taking, since he has some understanding of the problem. Before starting however, he should be aware of certain factors that enter into note taking. Students will find this a very difficult task at first. Everyone has a tendency to take too many notes. Do not try to record information that is generally known. Such material does not need documenting, and it is rather useless to copy extensive background material. The student should be careful to distinguish between facts and opinions. Bear in mind that facts are established data and are the basic information needed to develop the theme of the paper. Opinions will serve the purpose of adding weight to your own interpretations.

Sources are classed as primary (original) and secondary. A primary source is a first record of facts, or the closest a person using the material can come to the subject. Secondary source is material that has been taken from an original source. In a historical work primary sources are considered manuscripts, e.g., letters, diaries, and records or documents of various kinds. A secondary source is a work based on these original sources. In science primary sources are reports of observations or experiments, whereas secondary sources are accounts that are based on these reports. A student should try and use some original sources in his paper. The training he will receive in writing the paper will be so much greater, since he will have the opportunity of interpreting original data without being influenced by the opinions of others.

The writing of a reference paper calls for the exercise of judgment in evaluating the sources being used. This is difficult because the student has not done enough work in the field to be able to evaluate such sources. The only recourse is to rely on the opinion of others. Book reviews are a help in evaluating a book. Expressions of opinions about other sources or data are frequently found in your readings. Criticisms will occur in the literature about another's work. Such expressions can be of help in judging references. Such criticisms need recording, and should be noted on the bibliographic card or in a separate file. After a student has worked on a subject for some time he will learn to evaluate much of the material which will influence his choice of sources.

The paper on tuberculosis control presents an opportunity to use original documents as well as secondary sources, and also to consult with individuals who were acquainted with those who were instrumental in introducing the newer methods of tuberculosis control in the Lower Mississippi Valley. It will also serve as a good example of how your subject has to be limted to a smaller phase of the original topic you first outlined to investigate.

As mentioned previously the working bibliography card contained the complete bibliographic description of the reference. You now begin a new card file which is arranged by subject. These notes should be on 4 by 6 cards and include these three essential parts.

1. A symbol or heading to designate what the notes on the card treat.
2. The reference source, page, and volume if a set.
3. The material, facts, opinions, or data to be recorded.

In taking notes the first thing to remember is to assign a subject heading for classifying your information by the tentative outline. Classifying the material is difficult. It may be done in several ways. For broad general subjects colored guide cards may be used to designate subjects. In addition the top margin of the cards may be inked in colored ink or plain guide cards may be used with the subject divisions noted. If the paper is short any one of these methods is feasible, but if the paper is of some length then other methods have to be resorted to, such as making a subject index to the card file. In the upper right or left hand corner of the card list the specific subject heading chosen. This could be a sub-topic or the broad general subject mentioned previously.

The next information to record is the reference source.

There are two ways of doing this. One is simply by number. In the upper right or left hand corner record the number of the bibliographic item as numbered in the working bibliography. The other method is to list the author's name and an abbreviated title sufficient to identify the source in the opposite corner to the subject head ing. Be sure to record the exact page or pages and volume from which the information is taken. Paging may be entered in the left hand margin opposite the information or at the end of the note. Only one idea should be recorded on a card in order to simplify the classification. Be careful to enclose in quotation marks material that is copied directly. Your own comments should be enclosed in brackets to distinguish them from material taken from the sources. You may be doubtful at times where certain material will be used and for that reason make a "see" reference card. There can be no hard and fast rule in arranging the cards. Arranging them in some logical manner will tax the ingenuity of the writer.

An example of note taking cards is shown in Plate 13. In these examples the assigned subject heading is in the upper left hand corner and to the right is an abbreviated title of the reference. If the bibliographic file is numbered, then in the right hand corner would be listed the number for that reference. In the first example the pages from which this information is taken are listed in the left hand margin whereas in the second example the exact page is listed at the end of the note.

THE SENTENCE OUTLINE

The theme of your paper now begins to materialize as you complete the major part of your reading. From time to time as you become interested in a particular phase of the subject you begin to modify the tentative outline. In the subject used as an example, the work of Dr. Durel in

T.B.-History Brown, L.-Pulmonary
Four periods Tuberculosis
1. Beginning to the Middle of 17th Century
2. Remainder of 17th and 18th centuries
3. First three quarters of the 19 century
4. From the time Jean-Antoine Villemin (1827-92) proved the inoculability of T.B. (1864-9) to the discovery of the tubercle bacillus by Robert Koch (1843-1910) in 1882

Pg. 3-42

T.B. in New Orleans Barton-Report
Death Rate of Sanitory Comm.
Barton in 1849 reported the ratio of deaths from T.B. in New Orleans to be 1 in 16.65 and in 1854 he gave the ratio as 1 in 20.7 (table opposite p. 460)

Plate 13. Note Taking Cards.

introducing the newer methods of tuberculosis control in Louisiana becomes the dominant idea for the writing theme. Every fact assembled is in relation to his contribution. By this decision you have limited the subject to one phase of the original topic, the contribution of one man. The theme is now selected and the topic organized sufficiently to undertake a conclusive investigation. The revised outline or what is referred to as the sentence outline is now prepared. This is the outline which will guide you in the writing. The sentence outline is as follows:

Dr. Wallace Joseph Durel and the Sanatorium Movement in Louisiana

To study the contribution of Dr. Wallace Joseph Durel in introducing the sanatorium movement in Louisiana for the treatment of tuberculosis.

I. A review of the early history of tuberculosis in Louisiana is interesting but no conclusive evidence can be presented in regard to its incidence.
   A. Interesting figures can be presented from the records of Charity Hospital, and from the reports of Dr. Barton and Dr. Dowler.
   B. Some of the pre-sanatorium methods of treatment can be demonstrated by describing the methods of Dr. Hall and Dr. Cartwright.

II. The modern methods of tuberculosis control were introduced into Louisiana by Dr. Wallace Joseph Durel.
   A. The early career of Dr. Durel is interesting since it influenced his later interests in tuberculosis control.
   B. Dr. Durel's first efforts to establish a sanatorium, and his plan of management shows his insight and understanding of the advantages to be gained by employing the newer methods of tuberculosis control.
   C. His employment of artificial pneumothorax marks him as the first to make use of this method in this area.
   D. In his reports, Dr. Durel described the results obtained from his methods of treatment.

III. A summary of Dr. Durel's contribution shows some interesting trends in tuberculosis control in Louisiana.
   A. The newer methods of treatments as demonstrated by Dr. Durel showed the physicians of this area the advantages to be gained by such methods.
   B. The work of Dr. Durel was not limited to methods of treatment but included educating the public in tuberculosis prevention.

As you progress in writing, you must constantly review the facts that have been recorded in your notes from the standpont of what contribution they will make to the theme. There will be many references to sources that you will not have occasion to use. These should be critically evaluated and if the information given will not contribute anything to your problem discard it. Leaving irrelevant material in the working bibliography and notes will only make your task more difficult, because the card file will be cluttered up with useless information that will tend to make obscure the main theme of your paper. Evaluate each reference in regard to what it will contribute. Sometimes information is very interesting but adds nothing to the problem. If such information is discarded you will not be tempted to include such facts in your writing. You should refer to the sentence outline of your paper regarding all such questionable material. Where does this information belong? If there is no place for it, then eliminate it from your notes.

THE WRITING

After completing the sentence outline you are now ready to begin writing. The paper should be developed as follows: (1) Title; (2) Introduction; (3) Discussion; (4) Results, and (5) Summary and Conclusion.

The title should be short but not misleading. Avoid the too general title which means little to the reader; on the other extreme, do not be guilty of making the title too long.

The introduction is a very important part of any paper, and the statement in this part should lead into the discussion or body of the article. Make the introduction brief, simply a statement of the question involved, purpose, scope, general method of the investigation, and sometimes a list of sources. The danger is the tendency to make the introduction too long.

The discussion or body of the paper contains the development of the theme. Choose a logical order of events, basing this upon relation of events, importance, similarity or contrasts, complexity, and cause and effect. The order chosen should best serve the needs of clarity, coherence, and emphasis. Develop the main ideas so that they will be comprehensive to anyone, giving considerable thought to the relative importance of the several topics and their need of development. Illustrate the meaning of general or abstract statements by concrete examples. Point out the difference of opinion among scientists on the points involved. Be impersonal in your comments and avoid statements that are controversial.

The results should be a brief report of what was found. In a review paper the summary frequently takes the place of the results. The summary, a brief abstract of the article, may appear at the close. Not every article should be summarized. Those of more than average length (2,000 words), those which involve a lengthy description of detail and techniques, and those which aim at a complete survey of the literature on the subject require a summary.

The conclusion need not be as formal as in a more technical article, but should be adapted to the nature of the discussion or body of the article. It may be: (a) a summing up of points; (b) recommendations; (c) a combination of (a) and (b), and (d) general statements with the purpose of leaving a clear impression in the mind of the reader.

In the example used the introduction consists of the statement of the problem and that part of the sentence outline listed under section one, which outlines the status of tuberculosis in Louisiana. The discussion or body consists of section two, which presents the main theme as a series of events, their relationship and importance, and results obtained. The summary and conclusion, section three, is a summing up of Dr. Durel's contribution in introducing the newer methods of control in Louisiana.

THE STYLE

There is very little that can be said to guide the student in developing a good style. A style cannot be taught. It must be acquired through reading and practice. The best aids are dictionaries and the works of scholars. A few directives can be given in helping the student to present his facts. Employ words that are approved by good usage; avoid those that are obscure, ambiguous, or inappropriate. Define all terms that a reader might not understand. Avoid the use of the personal pronoun, particularly in scientific papers where the aim is to be objective rather than subjective. Present all material in a tactful way. Clear statements supported by evidence are better than positive assertions. For completeness of discussion it may be necessary to mention many points or facts that are well known, but do this tactfully so as not to annoy the reader.

Punctuation should follow current usage and should be uniform throughout the article. Rules for the use of abbreviations and figures are most frequently disregarded and, for that reason, the following suggestions are appended. In general no abbreviations should be used in the text. Titles (except Mr., Messrs., Mrs. and their foreign equivalent, Dr., St., Rev., Hon. preceding personal names, and Esq., Sr., and Jr. following names); names of states and months; the words "company" and "brothers" even when forming part of the names of a commercial firm; references to chapters, pages, lines, figures, plates, all should be spelled out in straight reading matter. In footnotes, bibliographic, and tabular matter, the abbreviation should be employed, as a rule. When dimensions, degrees, distances, and measures are used in the text combined with figures, they should be abbreviated as: 25.0 mg., 32 cc., 2 ft., 9 in., and 1200 km/sec. In isolated cases in the text matter, every number of less than two digits should be spelled out; however, all numbers used in a statistical connection should be expressed in figures. Round numbers, even if two digits or more, should be spelled out unless appearing with other figures in a statistical connection. Dates, pages, decimals, percentages should be expressed in figures, although the symbol for per cent should be spelled out. A number occurring at the beginning of a sentence must always be spelled out. Tenses are confusing at times. The following rules may be used as a guide.

1. Experimental facts should be given in the past tense. (The respiration of brain slices was affected by the higher concentration used.)

2. Remarks about the presentation of data should be mainly in the present tense. (These results are summarized in Table I.)

3. Discussion of results may be in both the past and present tenses, swinging back and forth from the experimental facts to the presentation. (When ACTH is injected in diabetic animals there is both a diabetogenic and catabolic nitrogen response by these animals though not to the same degree that was demonstrated by the control groups.)

4. Specific conclusions should be stated in the past tense. (The low plasma levels of vitamin A of patients with cancer were not due to a decreased capacity of the livers of those patients to store the vitamin.)

5. When a general truth is mentioned, it should be stated in the present tense. (The volume of gas varies inversely as the pressure.)

Trying to present the many practices that are considered good usage in a scholarly paper is beyond the scope of this text. For further information on this subject the student is referred to the recommended readings at the end of the text.

THE SCIENTIFIC PAPER

The above is a discussion of a reference paper which the student will be assigned to write first. Later, however, as he will be called upon to write papers reporting results from original investigations, and case reports, a brief résumé of some principles involved in preparing a scientific paper and case reports will be given. There is not too much difference between the presentation of a scientific paper, the facts of which are largely based on experimental data, and one whose facts have been compiled from the literature. This type of paper naturally consists of a report of facts and an interpretation of these facts. The important feature of such writing is that the plan of composition should be made very clear to the reader. The main divisions and their subdivisions should be plainly indicated, for a scientific paper is intended to be studied and used as a reference, not merely to be read. The outline given below has been drawn up from a study of the papers in *Science,* and should serve as a form for a variety of scientific papers.

I. Title.
II. Introduction:

- A. Status or description of problem.
- B. Purpose of investigation.

III. Materials and Methods:

- A. Apparatus and Instruments.
- B. Methods of procedure.
- C. Explanations of procedures.

IV. Results:

- A. Description of experiments.
- B. Description of results (tables and graphs).

V. Discussion of Results:

- A. Discussion of the findings of each variable.
- B. Interpretation and significance of each finding.
- C. Generalizations, explanation and causal relations.
- D. Conclusion drawn from results.

VI. Summary:

- A. Summarization of results.
- B. Suggestions for further study.

THE CASE REPORT

The foundation of clinical medical literature is the case report. Case reports or clinical notes are devoted to a single patient, illness, treatment, or minor clinical signs, symptoms, or procedures that deserve reporting. The simple case report may begin immediately with the history of the patient, or with the statement of why the author considers this case desirable to report. It should tell its story in a clear, straightforward narrative style. The form in which the report should be organized is as follows: the patient's history, family history, physical findings, laboratory findings, treatment, clinical course, results, and in case of death, postmortem observations. When a number of cases are reported with interpretations, the organization of the paper is similar to any other scholarly contribution. Following the title, and introduction, there may be a grouping of cases according to etiology, or treatment, or association with other diseases, to mention a few. A discussion follows with interpretations, conclusions and summary. Good examples of such papers are published in the *Quarterly Journal of Medicine.*

CHAPTER 3

DOCUMENTATION

THE MOST IMPORTANT phase of any scholarly publication is the documentation of the sources employed, and since this is so often neglected, the importance of this aspect in preparing a paper cannot be overemphasized. If there is one criterion by which the merits of a paper can be judged it is the character of its citations. It is an unfailing index to the care with which a manuscript has been prepared. If there is a lack of consistency in and poor arrangement of the references, it is very easy to infer that the writer is unsystematic in his thinking, and the preparation of his paper has been poor. The references to the sources utilized in the compilation of data are an integral part of any scientific investigation and should be stated clearly so that no one will have any trouble verifying a statement or fact. Then, too, it is only common courtesy to give credit where credit is due. The employment of facts calls for an evaluation of their sources so that a reader may judge for himself the evidence they are based on, and furthermore it permits one to use these facts if further information is desired. Therefore, a citation is an integral part of any scientific evidence. If it is not properly cited, an important step in your evidence is missing. No paper is ever completed until the author has verified his references. The chances of error are so many that no one should be satisfied until he has checked his references several times.

The purposes of a citation are two. It serves to give the exact source of a given statement or fact and also to describe the nature of the source. The first purpose emphasizes exactness and the second completeness. There are three methods of listing citations. The bibliography listed at the end of the paper, and the footnotes usually distributed throughout the paper or appended at the end are common to most general reference papers. A third method known as literature cited, or references, is employed in medicine and the allied sciences. In most instances it is a combination of the other two methods, and is used in short scientific papers. Each of these will be discussed in detail.

THE FINAL BIBLIOGRAPHY

A bibliography is commonly referred to as a list of the writings which relate to a given subject or author. This term is to some extent inaccurately used as applied to sources in a reference paper, since bibliography implies completeness, whereas the bibliography in a paper is in most cases a select list of the particular sources used. The term bibliography is usually employed in books or articles of a general nature where specific reference to the citation is not made in the text. In monographs a bibliography and specific references are both included. The final bibliography cannot be compiled or arranged until the paper is finished. There are three factors to keep in mind when compiling the final bibliography. These are content, form, and arrangement. Each one will be discussed in detail.

Content refers to the information required for a good bibliographic description, whereas form refers to the arrangement of this information. The minimum information required for a bibliographic description of a book is: (1) the author; (2) the title; (3) the place and/or publisher; (4) the date of publication, and (5) the pagination.

The matter of form and punctuation is of considerable importance in citing a reference. The author's last name is given first followed by his given name or initials. The author's name may be followed by either a period or comma. A comma or period follows the title. The title of a book is usually capitalized and underlined. An article or chapter in a book should be in quotations and small letters. Usually the place of publication as well as the publisher are given followed by the printing or copyright date. Practices vary in giving this information. Sometimes the place of publication is not given, only the publisher and date. Again the place may be given and not the publisher. The imprint may be inclosed in parentheses or it may not. The complete paging is given with the abbreviation "pp." or "p." either preceding or following the paging. There are several different forms in use for listing information about books. Some examples are as follows:

Boyd, William. *An Introduction to Medical Science,* 4th ed. Phila., Lea & Febiger, 1952. 304 p.

Boyd, William, *An Introduction to Medical Science,* 4th ed. (Philadelphia, 1952). 304 pp.

Stewart, Isabel Maitland, *The Education of Nurses.* New York: The Macmillan Company, 1943. pp. xi +399.

Correct reference to a part of a book or set:

Berens, Conrad. "Refraction." In: Piersol, G. M., ed.-in-chief. *The Cyclopedia of Medicine Surgery and Specialties,* v.13, p.558-66. Phila., Davis Co., c1945. 15v.

Jennings, H. S., "Heredity and environment in pediatrics," in Irvine McQuarrie, ed., *Brennemann's Practice of Pediatrics,* v.1, chap. 3, pp.1-28. Hagerstown, Maryland, Prior Co., 1952. 4v.

Caldwell, G. A., "The back, bones and joints," in Pullen, R. L., ed., *Medical Diagnosis; Applied Physical Diagnosis,* 2d ed., chap. 17, pp.812-69. Phila. and Lond., Saunders, 1950. 1119 pp.

Much that has been said with regard to citations to books can also be applied to journal articles. Every reference to a journal should contain: (1) the author's name; (2) the title; (3) the name of the journal in which the article appears; (4) the volume of the journal; (5) pagination, and (6) the date. Forms for journal citations have their own variations also. It is considered good practice in scientific citations to abbreviate the name of the journal. In abbreviating a title be sure to use one of the standard lists. The two standard lists that are commonly used in medicine and the allied sciences are the forms adopted by the *Quarterly Cumulative Index Medicus,* and the *Index-Catalogue of the Library of the Surgeon General's Office.* The abbreviations are listed in the front of every volume of the *Q.C.I.M.* and in volume B of the fourth series of the *Index-Catalogue.* Another list which is becoming more widely used is the list of abbreviations adopted by the *World List of Scientific Periodicals.* The forms adopted by the *Q.C.I.M.* and the *Index-Catalogue* are somewhat different. The same reference listed in each index has the following form:

Quarterly Cumulative Index Medicus

Padgett, E. C., Calibrated intermediate skin grafts, *Surg., Gynec. & Obst.* 69:779-793, Dec. '39

Index-Catalogue of the Surgeon General's Office

Padgett, E. C. Calibrated intermediate skin grafts. *Surg.Gyn.Obst.,* 1939, 69:779-93.

These entries show the pattern of scientific citations. The author's name may be followed by either a period or comma. The title may have a comma or period following it. The title of the journal is abbreviated with a comma or period following. In the first example the volume follows the title, and is separated from the paging by a colon. A comma follows the paging and then the date. In the second example the year follows the title, then a comma, the volume, a colon and paging. In scientific writings it is customary to use Arabic numbers for volumes instead of Roman numerals. The volume may be easily distinguished from the paging by a colon.

In the social sciences the form of listing citations is somewhat different. Examples of their citations are:

Sydnor, C. S. "Life Span of Mississippi Slaves," *American Historical Review,* XXXV (1930), 566-74.

Bischoff, Mary W. and Connolly, Mary G., "New Skills are Needed," *The American Journal of Nursing,* LI (September, 1951), 576-78.

The author's name may be followed by either a period or comma. The title of the article is enclosed in quotations followed by a comma. All principal words are capitalized. Roman numerals are still used for listing volume numbers followed by the date enclosed in parentheses. Journal titles are not abbreviated. A comma follows the date and the paging is given last.

Manuscript sources have their form also. It is good practice to give their location since they are not readily available. The following are examples:

Bayside, Plantation Records (1846-1852), Southern Historical Collection, University of North Carolina, Chapel Hill.

Davis, Hugh, Farm Journal (1848-1858), in possession of N. J. Davis, Marion, Alabama.

A number of other sources are frequently used such as public documents, reports, newspapers, and interviews. The following are examples of forms for such citations:

Probate Court Records of Adams County, Mississippi, Box 164-172, Record of Estates (1849-1908), Inventory and Appraisement Book No. 7.

U.S. Bureau of the Census, *Vital Statistics of the United States,* 1949. Part 1, Natality, mortality, marriage, divorce, morbidity and life table data for the United States. Wash., Government Printing Office, 1951. 2 pts.

New Orleans Daily True Delta, Nov. 26, 1857.

Statement by the late Mrs. Cammie Henry, Melrose, La., Sept. 15, 1950.

These examples show some of the many forms that have been adopted in listing bibliographic citations. They are all correct if they give the information required of a good bibliographic citation. The important thing to remember is to be consistent in using the same form throughout the bibliography. This principle is violated too frequently and indicates carelessness in the preparation of your paper.

The final factor is arrangement of your references. Arrangement of the references in a bibliography is very important because it demonstrates an intelligent and imaginative understanding of your problem and how you have presented and solved it. The basic arrangement for a bibliography is alphabetical by the author's last name or the first word in a title for which there is no author given. If there are two or more references by the same author a dash is substituted for the author's name the second time it is listed. In a short bibliography of not over 15 to 20 references the best arrangement is alphabetical. In a long paper where many references are given the best policy is to group the references according to some logical division. There are many divisions into which a bibliography may be divided. A few are: books, pamphlets, articles from periodicals, encyclopedic articles, government documents, manuscripts, interviews, contemporary material, noncontemporary material, theses and dissertations, hospital records, and newspapers. Items are alphabetically arranged under each grouping. In summary it should be stated again that a well prepared bibliography is the best criterion for evaluating how well you have presented your problem.

FOOTNOTES

Literature citations are also listed as "footnotes." They serve the purpose of giving a specific reference to an authority. Footnotes should be used for direct quotations, figures, dates, scientific data, opinions, and interpretations. The specific page or other means of identification is given so there will be no difficulty in identifying the exact source of the data. The footnotes may be scattered throughout the paper or appended at the end. In short papers they serve also as the bibliography.

There are several methods employed for handling such citations. They may be arranged alphabetically at the end of the paper and are then referred to in the text by the name of the author and the date, as for example (Smith, 1949). This has certain advantages as it easily permits the location of the citation in the alphabetical list at the end of the paper. It also permits deletion and additions to the citations without having to renumber the items. If there are several articles by Smith in the same year the suffixes, a, b, c, are added after the year. Another method refers to citations by numbers and they, too, may be appended at the end of the paper or scattered throughout. They are arranged numerically by the order in which they are referred to in the text. The numbering in the text is indicated by a superscript number or by numbers in parentheses. A third method employed is to arrange the citations alphabetically by the author's name. The citations are then numbered and reference in the text to the citations is by number.

In order to avoid repetition in a lengthy paper, a number of Latin abbreviations and abbreviated titles are commonly used. If a student wishes to use them, he should clearly understand their meaning and usage. Some of the commonly used Latin abbreviations are:

Ibid. (the same place). This should only be used for a reference identical to the one immediately preceding except for paging. If the page is different it may be added as *Ibid.,* 60. *Ibid.* should be underlined when referring to a published book or journal.

Idem. (the same man). This refers to the same person or author immediately preceding. This would probably be used only when the reference is to a different title than that immediately preceding and the new title must be given. A series of dashes is frequently used to indicate the same author.

Loc. cit. (in the place cited). May be used if the reference is to the same matter covered by a reference not immediately preceding. It must be preceded by the author's name, and cannot be used if more than one passage has been cited by this author.

Op. cit. (in the work quoted). May be used if the reference is to the same work of an author not immediately preceding. It must be preceded by the author's name, and should be followed by the exact page or pages.

f. or ff. These letters following a page number refer in the case of "f." to the page following, whereas "ff." is referring from the initial page to the end of the subject.

c (copyright). Copyright date of the book.

c. (circa). About.

An example of the use of these abbreviations is:

Foley, W. T., "Treatment of edema of the arm," *Surg.,Gynec. & Obst.* 93:568, Nov. 1951.

Clark, C. E., "Small intestinal obstruction due to endometriosis," *Am. Surgeon* 17:1145, Dec. 1951.

Ibid., 1147. (For a reference immediately following.)

Foley, *Loc. cit.* (For a reference not immediately following.)

Clark, *Op. cit.*, 1150. (For a reference not immediately following in which the citation is not to the same page.)

In cases where Latin abbreviations are not applicable or good form due to the length of the paper, abbreviated titles may be used for references to previously quoted citations. It is the practice to give the complete reference the first time a footnote is cited and the remaining times the Latin abbreviation or an abbreviated title or simply the author's name if that is sufficient to identify the source. Such examples are:

Ackerknect, Erwin H., *Malaria in the Upper Mississippi Valley,* 1760-1900. Baltimore, Johns Hopkins Press, 1945, p.101.

Ackerknect, *Malaria in the Mississippi Valley,* 106.

or

Ackerknect, 106.

Russell, P. F., "Some epidemiological aspects of malaria control with reference to DDT," *J.Nat.Malaria Soc.* 10:257, 1951.

Russell, 259.

It is the scholarly procedure in citing references to list both a bibliography and footnotes since the former gives a complete description and the latter the exact page reference for the authority of a statement or fact.

LITERATURE CITED OR REFERENCES

Medicine and its allied sciences have adopted another method of listing their citations. The reason probably is that in concise papers of this type there would be too much repetition, and since the citations are to short papers as a rule, references to specific pages are not necessary. The citations are similar to footnotes and are either scattered throughout the paper or appended at the end. In either case they serve as the bibliography but are listed as footnotes since reference is made in the text to specific citations. They may be arranged alphabetically at the end of the paper or listed numerically as they are referred to in the text. The citations are referred to as "Literature Cited" or "References."

There are two forms for listing the citations. In one case a complete bibliographic description is given for each citation. Usually references are to journals so the citation will include the author, title of article, journal, volume, paging, and date. In the other case only the author, journal, volume, first page of the article, and date are given. There is no reference to a specific page, which is a handicap for tracing a source in an article of some length. This disadvantage may be overcome in a number of ways. If the citations are numbered in the text, instead of simply listing the number of the citation give also the page number following the citation as for example (2:166). The number two refers to the number of the citation and 166 to the page. If the citations are referred to in the text by the author and date then give the page following as for example (Smith, 1949, p.104). These two examples break the continuity of the text somewhat so it is probably better to list the exact page if that is necessary following the citation in the footnotes or references. This can be done by enclosing the exact page reference in brackets or parentheses following the reference.

FINAL RECOMMENDATIONS

It is very difficult to recommend any hard and fast rule for the arrangement of citations. Each paper should be judged as an individual problem. Whether the references are arranged alphabetically, numerically, or by date with specific references or only general citations with no reference from the text depends upon the material and its presentation. Every author should feel a grave responsibility for the accuracy and logical arrangement of his references. If the paper is being prepared for publication then the references should be arranged in accordance with the conventions of the journal to which it is to be submitted. In conclusion, remember never to take your data from a secondary source if it is at all possible to check the primary source, because the chances of error are multiplied many times. Then, finally, never forget to verify your references. You can never check them enough to be certain no errors have crept in. The responsibility of the author is great where his citations are concerned. If you acquire the habit of carefully recording the references the task will never seem difficult, and you will have the satisfaction of knowing that your paper has been well done.

APPENDIX I

TEXTS REFERRED TO IN PART II

DICTIONARIES

Blakiston's New Gould Medical Dictionary. Philadelphia, Blakiston, 1949, 1294 pp.

Dorland, W. A. N.: *The American Illustrated Medical Dictionary*, 22nd Ed. Philadelphia, Saunders, 1951, 1736 pp.

Dunning, W. B. and Davenport, S. E., Jr.: *A Dictionary of Dental Science and Art*. Philadelphia, Blakiston, 1936, 635 pp.

Fairchild, H. P.: *Dictionary of Sociology*. New York, Philosophical Library, 1944, 342 pp.

Good, C. V.: *Dictionary of Education*. New York, McGraw-Hill, 1945, 495 pp.

Funk and Wagnalls New Standard Dictionary of the English Language. New York, Funk and Wagnalls, 1952, 2815 pp.

Funk and Wagnalls Standard Dictionary of Folklore, Mythology and Legend. New York, Funk and Wagnalls, c1949-1950, 2v.

Gordon, Alfred: *French-English Medical Dictionary*. Philadelphia, Blakiston, c1921, 161 pp.

Hackh, I. W. D.: *Chemical Dictionary*, 3rd Ed. Philadelphia, Blakiston, 1950, 925 pp.

Harriman, P. L.: *The New Dictionary of Psychology*. New York, Philosophical Library, c1947, 364 pp.

Hinsie, L. E. and Shatzky, Jacob: *Psychiatric Dictionary*, 2nd Ed. New York, Oxford, 1953, 781 pp.

Karel, Leonard and Roach, E. S.: *A Dictionary of Antibiosis*. New York, Columbia University Press, 1951, 373 pp.

Lang, Hugo: *German-English Dictionary of Terms Used in Medicine and the Allied Sciences*, 4th Ed. Philadelphia, Blakiston, c1932, 926 pp.

Marconi, Ruggero and Zino, Elena: *Dizionario Inglese-Italiano per le Scienze Mediche*. Torino, Edizioni Minerva Medica, [1949], 565 pp.

Marie, J. S. F.: *English, German, French, Italian, Spanish Medical Vocabulary and Phrases*. Philadelphia, Blakiston, c1939, 358 pp.

Miall, Stephen and Miall, L. M.: *A New Dictionary of Chemistry*, 2nd Ed. London, Longmans, Green, c1949, 589 pp.

Price, A. L.: *The American Nurses Dictionary*. Philadelphia, Saunders, 1949, 659 pp.

Schoenewald, F. S.: *German-English Medical Dictionary*. Philadelphia, Blakiston, 1949, 241 pp.

Stedman, T. L.: *Stedman's Medical Dictionary*, 18th Ed. Baltimore, Williams and Wilkins, 1953, 1561 pp.

Veillon, Emmanuel: *Medical Dictionary. Dictionnaire Médical. Medizinisches Wörterbuch.* New York, Grune and Stratton, c1950, 476 pp.

Warren, H. C.: *Dictionary of Psychology.* Boston, Houghton Mifflin, c1934, 372 pp.

Webster, Noah: *New International Dictionary of the English Language,* 2nd Ed. unabr. repr. Springfield, Mass., Merriam, 1951, 3214 pp.

Webster, Noah: *Webster's Dictionary of Synonyms.* Springfield, Mass., Merriam, c1942, 907 pp.

DIRECTORIES

American Dental Directory, 1954. Chicago, American Dental Association, 1953, 1077 pp.

American Foundations and Their Fields, 6th Ed. New York, Raymond Rich Associates, 1948, 284 pp.

American hospital directory. *Hospitals,* June, pt.2.

American Medical Association. Council on Medical Education and Hospitals: Approved internships and residencies in the United States. *J.A.M.A.,* Int.&Res.No.

American Medical Association. Council on Medical Education and Hospitals: Hospital service in the United States. *J.A.M.A.,* Hosp.No.

American Medical Association. Council on Medical Education and Hospitals: Medical education in the United States and Canada. *J.A.M.A.,* Educ.No.

American Medical Directory, 18th Ed. Chicago, American Medical Association, 1950, 2913 pp.

Catholic hospital directory. *Hosp.Progr.,* Suppl.

Cattell, Jacques: *American Men of Science,* 9th Ed. New York, Bowker, 1955-56, 3v. In press.

Current Biography. New York, Wilson, 1940+, v.1+.

Dictionary of American Biography. New York, Scribner, 1943 repr., 21v.

Dictionary of National Biography. New York, Oxford University Press, 1938 repr., 22v.

Directory of Medical Specialists, Vol. 7. Chicago, Marquis, 1955, 2214 pp.

Kelly, H. A. and Burrage, W. L.: *Dictionary of American Medical Biography.* New York, Appleton, 1928, 1364 pp.

Medical Directory, 1953. London, Churchill, 1953, 2v.

National Research Council: *Handbook of Scientific and Technical Societies and Institutions of the United States and Canada,* 5th Ed. Washington, National Research Council, 1948, 371 pp. (Nat.Res.Counc.Bull., no. 115, 1948.)

Patterson's American Educational Directory, Vol. 50. Wilmette, Ill., Educational Directories, c1953, 737 pp.

Schnapper, M. B.: *American Health Directory.* Washington, Public Affairs Press, c1952, 96 pp.

Who Was Who, 1897-1950. New York, Macmillan, 1929-1952, 4v.
Who Was Who in America, 1897-1950. Chicago, Marquis, 1942-1950, 2v.
Who's Who, Vol. 105. New York, Macmillan, 1953, 3277 pp.
Who's Who in America, 1954-1955, Vol. 28. Chicago, Marquis, c1954, 3370 pp.
Who's Who in World Medicine, 1939. London, B. U. E., c1939, 605 pp.

ENCYCLOPEDIAS

American Pharmaceutical Association: *The National Formulary,* 9th Ed. Washington, American Pharmaceutical Association, 1950, 877 pp.
Brennemann, Joseph: *Practice of Pediatrics.* Hagerstown, Md., Prior, 1936+, 4v.
The Cyclopedia of Medicine, Surgery, Specialties. Philadelphia, Davis, c1950+, 14v.
Davis, C. H.: *Gynecology and Obstetrics.* Hagerstown, Md., Prior, 1933+, 3v.
The Dispensatory of the United States of America, 24th Ed. Philadelphia, Lippincott, 1950, 2057 pp.
Encyclopaedia Britannica, 14th Ed. Chicago, Encyclopaedia Britannica, 1949, 24v.
Encyclopedia Americana. New York and Chicago, Americana Corporation, 1953, 30v.
The Encyclopedia of Nursing. Philadelphia, Saunders, c1952, 1011 pp.
Encyclopedia of the Social Sciences. New York, Macmillan, 1930-1935, 15v.
Gaynor, Frank: *Pocket Encyclopedia of Atomic Energy.* New York, Philosophical Library, c1950, 204 pp.
Langer, W. L.: *An Encyclopedia of World History,* Rev. Ed. Boston, Houghton Mifflin, 1952, 1243 pp.
Lewis, Dean: *Practice of Surgery.* Hagerstown, Md., Prior, 1927+, 12v.
Merck Index of Chemicals and Drugs, 6th Ed. Rahway, N.J., Merck, 1952, 1167 pp.
Modern Drug Encyclopedia and Therapeutic Index, 5th Ed. New York, Drug Publications, c1952, 1431 pp.
Monroe, W. S.: *Encyclopedia of Educational Research,* Rev. Ed. New York, Macmillan, 1950, 1520 pp.
The Oxford Medicine. New York, Oxford University Press, 1920+, 8v.
Pharmacopoeia of the United States of America, 14th Ed. Rev. By the authority of the U. S. Pharmacopoeia Convention, Inc. Easton, Pa., Mack, 1950, 1122 pp.
Tice, Frederick: *Practice of Medicine.* Hagerstown, Md., Prior, 1920+, 10v.

INDEXES

Books in Print, 1948+. New York, Bowker, 1948+.
Cumulative Book Index, 1928+. New York, Wilson, 1933+.

Current List of Medical Literature, 1941+. Washington, Armed Forces Medical Library, 1941+, v.1+.

Education Index, 1929+. New York, Wilson, 1932+, v.1+.

Garrison, F. H. and Morton, L. T.: *A Medical Bibliography,* 2nd Ed. London, Grafton, In press.

Index-Catalogue of the Library of the Surgeon General's Office, United States Army, 1880-1948. Washington, Government Printing Office, 1880-1948, Ser. 1-4, v.1-10 (Ser. 1-3 compl. Ser. 4 in progress).

Index Medicus, 1879-1927. New York, Boston, and Washington, 1879-1927, Ser. 1-3, v.1-6, no.5.

Index of Hospital Literature, 1945+. Chicago, American Hospital Association, 1950+.

Index to Dental Literature in the English Language, 1939+. Chicago, American Dental Association, 1943+. (Continuation of A. D. Black's *Index of the Periodical Dental Literature Published in the English Language, 1839-1936/38.)*

International Index to Periodicals, 1907+. New York, Wilson, 1916+, v.1+.

Kelly, E. C.: *Encyclopedia of Medical Sources.* Baltimore, Williams & Wilkins, 1948, 476 pp.

Public Affairs Information Service. Bulletin, 1915+. New York, Public Affairs Information Service, 1915+, v.1+.

Publishers' Trade List Annual, 1873+. New York, Bowker, 1873+.

Quarterly Cumulative Index Medicus, 1927+. Chicago, American Medical Association, 1927+, v.1+.

Quarterly Cumulative Index to Current Medical Literature, 1916-1926. Chicago, American Medical Association, 1917-1927, 12v.

Readers' Guide to Periodical Literature, 1900+. New York, Wilson, 1905+, v.1+.

Technical Book Review Index, 1935+. Pittsburgh, Special Libraries Association, 1935+, v.1+.

Ulrich's Periodicals Directory, 7th Ed. New York, Bowker, 1953, 684 pp.

Union List of Serials in Libraries of the United States and Canada, 2nd Ed. New York, Wilson, 1943, 3065 pp.

——— *Supplement, 1941-1943.* New York, Wilson, 1945, 1123 pp.

——— *Second Supplement, 1944-1949.* New York, Wilson, In progress.

United States. Armed Forces Medical Library: *Catalog, Apr./Dec., 1948+.* Washington, Library of Congress, 1948+.

United States Catalog; Books in Print, January 1, 1928, 4th Ed. New York, Wilson, 1928, 3164 pp.

United States. Superintendent of Documents: *United States Government Publications; Monthly Catalog, 1895+.* Washington, Government Printing Office, 1895+.

World List of Scientific Periodicals Published in the Years 1900-1950,

3rd Ed. New York, Academic Press; London, Butterworths, 1952, 1058 pp.

World Medical Periodicals. Natural Sciences Division, UNESCO, [1952], 237 pp.

YEARBOOKS

American Medical Association. Council on Pharmacy and Chemistry: *New and Nonofficial Remedies, 1909+.* Chicago, American Medical Association; Philadelphia, Lippincott, 1909+.

Americana Annual, 1923+. New York, Americana Corporation, 1923+, v.1+.

Britannica Book of the Year, 1938+. Chicago, Encyclopaedia Britannica, 1938+.

Current Therapy, 1949+. Philadelphia, Saunders, 1949+.

Monographs on Surgery, 1950+. New York, Nelson; Baltimore, Williams and Wilkins, 1949+.

Physicians' Desk Reference, 1947+. Rutherford, N.J., Medical Economics, 1946+.

Social Work Year Book, 1929+. New York, Russell Sage Foundation; American Association of Social Workers, 1930+, v.1+.

United States. Bureau of the Census: *Statistical Abstract of the United States, 1878+.* Washington, Government Printing Office, 1879+, v.1+.

World Almanac and Book of Facts, 1868+. New York, New York World Telegram, 1868+, v.1+.

Appendix II

RECOMMENDED READINGS

PART I

Ballard, J. F.: Medieval manuscripts and early printed books illustrating the evolution of the medical book from 1250 to 1550 A.D. *Bull.M.Library A., 23*:173-188, 1935.

Billings, J. S.: A century of American medicine, 1776-1876, literature and institutions. *Am.J.M.Sc., 72*:439-480, 1876.

Billings, J. S.: The medical journals of the United States. *Boston M.& S.J., 100*:1-14, 1879.

Breasted, J. H.: *The Edwin Smith Surgical Papyrus.* Chicago, University of Chicago Press, 1930, 2v.

Brim, C. J.: *Medicine in the Bible.* New York, Froben, 1936, 384 pp.

Butler, Pierce: *The Origin of Printing in Europe.* Chicago, University of Chicago Press, c1940, 154 pp.

Crummer, Le Roy: A glimpse at the early development of medical literature. In *Contributions to the Medical Sciences in Honor of Dr. Emanuel Libman,* Vol. 1. New York, International Press, c1932, 3v., pp. 345-356.

Dawson, W. R.: *The Beginnings, Egypt and Assyria.* New York, Hoeber, c1930, 86 pp.

An earlier "British Medical Journal"? *Brit.M.J., 2*:777, 1936.

Garrison, F. H.: *An Introduction to the History of Medicine,* 4th Ed. Philadelphia, Saunders, c1929, 996 pp.

Gask, G. E.: Early medical schools; Cyrene, Cos and Cnidos. *AnnM.Hist., 2*:15-21, 1940.

Greco, Vincent: The origin of medical journalism. *New York M.J., 97*: 131-136, 1913.

Horner, N. B.: Medical journalism in the British Empire. *Lancet, 2*:273-274, 1932.

LeFanu, W. R.: British periodicals of medicine. *Bull.Inst.Hist.Med., 5*: 735-761, 827-855, 1937.

Lund, F. B.: *Greek Medicine.* New York, Hoeber, 1936, 161 pp.

MacKinney, L. C.: *Early Medieval Medicine.* Baltimore, Johns Hopkins Press, c1937, 247 pp.

Ornstein, Martha: *The Role of Scientific Societies in the Seventeenth Century.* Chicago, University of Chicago Press, c1938, 308 pp.

Phalen, J. M.: American medical literature-1836. *M.Life, 43*:580-587, 1936.

Phemister, D. B.: Ancient medical manuscripts during the Middle Ages and their recovery at the end of that period. *Bull.Soc.M.Hist.Chicago, 5*:150-158, 1939.

Singer, C. J.: A review of the medical literature of the Dark Ages, with a new text of about 1110. *Proc.Roy.Soc.Med.(Sect.Hist.Med.), 10:*107-160, 1917.

PART II

Alexander, Carter, *et al.: How to Locate Educational Information and Data,* 3rd Ed. New York, Bureau of Publications, Teachers College, Columbia University, 1950, 441 pp.

Brodman, Estelle: The contribution of the Army Medical Library to the bibliographic control of Medical literature. *Special Libraries, 43:*48-54, 73-76, 1952.

Brodman, Estelle: *The Development of Medical Bibliography.* [Baltimore], Medical Library Association, 1954, 226 pp.

Medical Library Association: *Handbook of Medical Library Practice,* 2nd Ed. Chicago, American Library Association, In press.

Morton, L. T.: *How to Use a Medical Library,* 2nd Ed. London, Heinemann, 1952, 44 pp.

New York University. College of Dentistry. Library: *Library Manual of the New York University, College of Dentistry, by Helen Hlavac,* Librarian, 2nd Ed. [New York], c1950, 58 pp.

Tennessee. University. Library: *Library Orientation and Instruction Syllabus,* Rev. Ed. Memphis, Library, University of Tennessee, 1952, 110 pp.

Thornton, J. L.: *Medical Books, Libraries, and Collectors.* London, Grafton, 1949, 293 pp.

PART III

Almack, J. C.: *Research and Thesis Writing.* Boston, Houghton Mifflin, c1930, 310 pp.

Baer, K. A.: Bibliographical methods in the biological sciences. *Special Libraries, 45:*74-80, 1954.

Chicago. University. Press: *A Manual of Style,* 11th Ed. Chicago, University of Chicago Press, 1949, 497 pp.

Crowe, M. R.: An introduction to the preparation and writing of articles for medical journals. *Jefferson-Hillman Hosp.Bull., 4:*59-98, 1950.

Fishbein, Morris and Whelan, J. F.: *Medical Writing,* 2nd Ed. Philadelphia, Blakiston, c1948, 292 pp.

Fulton, J. F.: The principles of bibliographical citation. *Bull.M.Library A., 22:*183-197, 1934.

Hook, Lucyle and Gaver, M. V.: *The Research Paper.* New York, Prentice-Hall, 1948, 64 pp.

Jordan, E. P. and Shepard, W. C.: ℞ *for Medical Writing.* Philadelphia, Saunders, 1952, 112 pp.

Perrin, P. G.: *Writer's Guide and Index to English,* Rev.Ed. Chicago, Scott, Foresman, c1950, 833 pp.

Schrero, Morris: Bibliographic technique. *Special Libraries,* 30:302-306, 1939.

Thomas, P. E. L.: *A Guide for Authors on Manuscript, Proof, and Illustration.* Springfield, Thomas, c1949, 85 pp.

Trelease, S. F.: *The Scientific Paper.* Baltimore, Williams & Wilkins, 1947, 152 pp.

Whitney, F. L.: *The Elements of Research,* 3rd Ed. New York, Prentice-Hall, 1950, 539 pp.

APPENDIX III

STUDY QUESTIONS

Part I

HISTORICAL BIBLIOGRAPHY

Chapter 1. The Manuscript

1. What contribution to science did the three ancient cultures mentioned in the text make?
2. What conditions existed in Greece that were conducive to the beginning of a natural explanation of nature's laws?
3. Who was Hippocrates and what did he contribute to scientific medicine?
4. Describe the influence Galen had on medicine for centuries to come.
5. What contribution did the Arabs make in preserving Greek culture?
6. In what manner were Greek writings reintroduced into Western Europe?
7. Describe the medical book of the later Middle Ages.

Chapter 2. The Book

1. What influence did the vernacular writings which appeared between 1535-1540 have on medical culture?
2. Describe the medical book of 1470-1540.

Chapter 3. The Journal

1. What effect did the development of scientific and medical societies have on medical writings?
2. Scientific journalism began with the appearance of what journal? Did it prove a success?
3. What was the first medical journal? What effect did it have on the spread of medical knowledge?
4. What concept did Thomas Wakley have of medical journalism? What influence did the *Lancet* have on medical journalism?
5. What was the status of medical literature in America prior to the Revolution?
6. What effect did the *Medical Repository* have on medical advancement in this country?
7. What were the three methods of editing the early journals in America?
8. What change did the *J.A.M.A.* introduce in medical journalism?
9. What are some of the more recent developments of medical journalism?

Part II

MODERN BIBLIOGRAPHY

Chapter 1. The Medical Library and its Organization

1. What is the function of a medical library?
2. In a general way how are the books and journals arranged in a medical library?

Chapter 2. Indexes to the Book Collection

1. What is the importance of booklists or catalogs?
2. Name the important book catalogs giving contents and arrangement of each.
3. Discuss the principal features of the card catalog, including types of cards, arrangement, bibliographic information, and filing rules.

Chapter 3. Basic Reference Books

1. What are reference books?
2. What are the qualities of a good reference book?
3. What are the principal features of the two unabridged English language dictionaries?
4. What is the purpose of foreign language, special, and medical dictionaries?
5. What are the two categories of directories?
6. What are the principal features (coverage, arrangement) of the general, special, and medical directories?
7. What are the special features of the two general encyclopedias listed in the text?
8. What other types of encyclopedias are there? What are the characteristics of each?
9. What are yearbooks? What types are there? What are their principal features?
10. What do the various drug reference books purport to do?

Chapter 4. Indexes to the Periodical Collection

1. What are the principal features of a periodical index? Discuss the importance of scope, length of period covered, frequency and promptness of publication, the completeness and quality of indexing.
2. What types of reference aids does a library need to answer the ordinary questions about periodicals?
3. What are the principal bibliographies of periodicals and what purpose do they serve?
4. What is the purpose of the serial record? What two listings are used by libraries? What are some of the advantages and disadvantages of each?
5. Discuss the general periodical indexes. What periodicals do they index? What is their arrangement, cumulative features, and coverage?
6. Do the same for the special indexes.

7. What are the problems faced in medical indexing?
8. Discuss the principal medical indexes giving the type of material indexed, arrangement, frequency, and purpose.
9. What do abstract journals purport to do? What are some of the principal ones?
10. What are cumulative indexes and what purpose do they serve?

Chapter 5. The Periodical Collection

1. What is the importance of periodicals in a medical library?
2. Discuss their format and their arrangement in the library.
3. Into what groups can journals be divided?
4. After examining a number of journals be able to discuss the date, volume, and number examined, type of articles, book reviews, abstracts, indexes, and any other special features noted.
5. Explain the purpose of review journals.

Part III

METHODS OF BIBLIOGRAPHY

Chapter 1. Principles of Scientific Investigation

1. What is science and what are some of its methods of investigation?
2. What is your understanding of the hypothesis and the part it plays in scientific investigation?
3. What is the bibliographic approach to scientific investigation?

Chapter 2. The Reference Paper

1. What types of reference papers are there?
2. What are some of the points to be considered in selecting a topic to investigate?
3. What are the principal procedures in acquiring facts? What tools do you use?
4. Discuss procedures and proper methods of taking notes.
5. What are the parts of a reference paper? How does this compare with a scientific paper?

Chapter 3. Documentation

1. What is the purpose of citations?
2. What is a bibliography? In what type of paper is it most frequently used? Discuss the contents, form, and arrangement of the bibliography.
3. What are footnotes? What purpose do they serve? Discuss their form and arrangement.
4. What are some of the commonly used Latin abbreviations? How are they used?
5. What are abbreviated titles and how are they used in footnotes?
6. Explain the use of citations as literature cited or references.
7. What criteria would you use in arranging a bibliography, footnotes, and references or literature cited?

INDEX

This Book

APPLIED MEDICAL BIBLIOGRAPHY FOR STUDENTS

By

WILLIAM DOSITE POSTELL

was set and printed by The Ovid Bell Press, Inc., of Fulton, Missouri. It was bound by the Becktold Company of St. Louis, Missouri. The engravings were made by Capitol Engraving Company of Springfield, Illinois. The page trim size is 5½ x 8½ inches. The type page is 23 x 39 picas. The type face is Baskerville, set 11 point on 13 point. The text paper is 70 lb. Carfax Eggshell. The cover is Roxite LS Vellum, 5175, 11-M, two-tone, black.